Earth Science Lab Exercises

James W. Fatherree and James F. Wysong, Jr.

ISBN 0-9786194-2-0

Published by:
Liquid Medium Publications
Tampa, Florida

Earth Science Lab Exercises

Table of Contents

Lab 1: Units of Measure	1	Lab 1 answers:	96
Lab 2: Earth-Sun Relations	6	Lab 2 answers:	99
Lab 3: Humidity	12	Lab 3 answers:	102
Lab 4: Air Masses, Fronts, and Weather Maps	18	Lab 4 answers:	105
Lab 5: Severe Weather	25	Lab 5 answers:	108
Lab 6: Topographic Maps Pt.1	28	Lab 6 answers:	111
Lab 7: Topographic Maps Pt.2	33	Lab 7 answers:	112
Lab 8: Topographic Maps Pt.3	38	Lab 8 answers:	114
Lab 9: Minerals and Mineral Identification	42	Lab 9 answers:	115
Lab 10: Rocks and Rock Identification	49	Lab 10 answers:	116
Lab 11: Streams	58	Lab 11 answers:	117
Lab 12: Earth's Structure and Plate Tectonics	64	Lab 12 answers:	120
Lab 13: Seismic Waves and Earthquakes	69	Lab 13 answers:	123
Lab 14: Volcanoes and Other Igneous Features	75	Lab 14 answers:	125
Lab 15: Waves and the Tides	80	Lab 15 answers:	127
Lab 16: Radiometric Dating	84	Lab 16 answers:	128
Lab 17: Fossils and Stratigraphy	87	Lab 17 answers:	130

Lab 1: Units of Measure

It is important to know units of measure in this course, and in life in general. So, this lab will familiarize you with the U.S. Customary and metric systems of measurement and how to convert various units of measure, especially those related to distance that will be used in this course. Understanding density and the things that affect it are also important, as density plays a role many phenomena and processes. Thus, it will be covered in this lab, as well.

Objectives:

1) Learn the common U.S. Customary units of measure.

2) Learn the common metric units of measure.

3) Learn how to convert units of distance within the U.S. Customary system.

4) Learn how to convert units of distance within the metric system.

5) Learn how to convert units of measure between U.S. Customary and metric systems.

6) Learn about density and how to calculate the density of a material.

Part I

Here in the United States we primarily use the U.S. Customary system of measurement. Frankly, it is outdated and difficult to use, especially when it comes to the conversion of units. However, it's what we still use, so you should know it.

Mass: The U.S. Customary system uses ounces, pounds, and tons as basic units of mass. One ton equals 2,000 pounds, and one pound equals 16 ounces.

Distance: The U.S. Customary system uses inches, feet, and miles as basic units of distance. One mile equals 5,280 feet, and one foot equals 12 inches.

> **1 mile = 5,280 feet = 63,360 inches**
>
> **1 foot = 12 inches**

Atmospheric Pressure: Atmospheric pressure as measured using a standard mercury barometer is typically given as inches of mercury, and standard atmospheric pressure (the average pressure at sea level) is 29.92 inches of mercury.

Temperature: Temperature is measured in degrees Fahrenheit. The only two temperatures of note are the freezing point of water, 32°F, and its boiling point, 212°F. Also note that the boiling point is affected by pressure. When atmospheric pressure decreases, water will boil at a temperature lower than 212°F, and at higher pressures the boiling point increases.

Part II

You will need to know how to convert U.S. Customary units of distance from one unit to another. If you know the value of different units this can be done quite easily, so make sure to learn them.

If you are converting a larger unit to a smaller unit, just multiply the value of the larger unit by the number of smaller units that will fit into the larger. For example, to convert 3 miles to feet, multiply 3 by 5,280 since 5,280 feet equals 1 mile. The answer is 3 x 5,280 = 15,840 feet.

Conversely, if you are converting a smaller unit to a larger unit, divide the value of the smaller unit by the number of that unit that will fit into the larger. For example, to convert 10,000 feet to miles, divide 10,000 by 5,280 since 5,280 feet equals 1 mile. The answer is 10,000 / 5,280 = 1.89 miles.

Complete the following sentences, rounding figures to the nearest tenth:

1) There are _1,080_ inches in 90 feet.

2) There are _6_ inches in 0.5 feet.

3) There are _126,720_ inches in 2 miles.

4) There are _26,400_ feet in 5 miles.

5) There are _3168_ feet in 0.6 miles.

6) A distance of 730 inches equals a distance of _60.83_ feet.

7) A distance of 262,000 inches equals a distance of _4.14_ miles.

8) A distance of 14,000 feet equals a distance of _2.65_ miles.

9) A distance of 3 miles equals a distance of _190,080_ inches.

10) A distance of 7 miles equals a distance of _36,960_ feet.

Part III

Now we get to the metric system of measurement, which is used by every major country in the world, except the United States. Still, even though it's not officially used here, it's creeping into our lives a little at a time. For example, we used to say a Chevy Corvette had a 350 cubic inch motor, but now we say it has a 5.7 liter motor. Likewise, many Ford Mustangs had 302 cubic inch motors, which were called "5.0s" (liters) later. Aspirin comes in milligrams, liquor comes in 750 milliliter bottles, sodas come in 2 liter bottles, and some people run 5k (kilometer) races, etc. So, metric is around to some degree.

Regardless of its general lack of use here, it's much easier to deal with than the U.S. Customary system. It's based on units of 10, which makes it simple to convert things to larger or smaller units of measure. So, what you need to focus on are a few prefixes and their meanings.

Starting with a base unit, the prefix *mill* can be placed in front of it, which means 1,000th. Or, the prefix *cent* can be placed in front of it, which means 100th. Or, the prefix *kilo* can be placed in front of it, which means 1,000.

For example, you might buy a 1 liter bottle of soda. A milliliter of that soda would be 1,000th the volume of the bottle. In other words, a 1 liter bottle of soda holds 1,000 milliliters. And, if you have a stick that is 1 meter long, a centimeter would be 100th the length of the stick. In other words, a 1 meter stick is the same thing as a 100 centimeter stick. Likewise, if you bought a packet of sugar that weighed 1 gram, you'd need to buy 1,000 packets to have a kilogram of sugar. In other words, 1 kilogram of sugar is the same thing as 1,000 grams of sugar, so each 1 gram packet would be 1,000th of a kilogram.

There are other prefixes (deci, deca, nano, pico, micro, etc.), but these are rarely used in day to day applications of measurement. We'll stick primarily with what is most important for this course, which are units related to distance.

Mass: The metric system uses kilograms, grams, and milligrams as basic units of mass. One kilogram equals 1,000 grams, and one gram equals 1,000 milligrams.

Distance: The metric system uses kilometers, meters, centimeters, and millimeters as basic units of distance. One kilometer equals 1,000 meters, one meter equals 100 centimeters, and one centimeter equals 10 millimeters.

Mass = gram
Volume = liter
Distance = meter

1 kilometer	= 1,000 meters	= 100,000 centimeters
1 meter	= 100 centimeters	= 1,000 millimeter
1 centimeter	= 10 millimeters	

milli = 1/1000
cent = 1/100
kilo = 1000

Atmospheric Pressure: Atmospheric pressure as measured using a standard mercury barometer is typically given as millibars, and standard atmospheric pressure (the average pressure at sea level) is approximately 1,013 millibars (1.01325 bars).

Temperature: Temperature is measured in degrees Celsius (formerly called centigrade). The only two temperatures of note are the freezing point of water, 0°C, and its boiling point, 100°C. Again, the boiling point is affected by pressure.

Part IV

You will also need to know how to convert metric units of distance from one unit to another. This works the same way for the metric system as it does for the U.S. Customary system.

If you are converting a larger unit to a smaller unit, just multiply the value of the larger unit by the number of smaller units that will fit into the larger. For example, to convert 3 kilometers to meters, multiply 3 by 1,000 since 1,000 meters equals 1 kilometer. The answer is 3 x 1,000 = 3,000 meters.

Conversely, if you are converting a smaller unit to a larger unit, divide the value of the smaller unit by the number of that unit that will fit into the larger. For example, to convert 6,000 meters to kilometers, divide 6,000 by 1,000 since 1,000 meters equals 1 kilometer. The answer is 6,000 / 1,000 = 6 km.

Complete the following sentences, rounding figures to the nearest tenth:

11) There are ___4000___ centimeters in 40 meters. 100 x 40

12) There are ___30___ centimeters in 0.3 meters.

13) There are ___200,000___ centimeters in 2 kilometers.

14) There are ___5,000___ meters in 5 kilometers.

15) There are ___400___ meters in 0.4 kilometers.

16) A distance of 850 centimeters equals a distance of ___8.5___ meters.

17) A distance of 122,000 centimeters equals a distance of ___1.22___ kilometers.

18) A distance of 14,000 meters equals a distance of ___14___ kilometers.

19) A distance of 4 kilometers equals a distance of ___400,000___ centimeters.

3

Part V

You should also be able to use the common units of measure in both systems interchangeably, and thus should be able to convert units of one system to those of the other. Again, we will primarily focus on those that will be used in this course and the lecture. The conversion factors are shown below, but you are not required to learn these. You only need to learn how to carry out the conversions, as the factors will be provided on any quiz/exam.

U.S. Customary and Metric Conversions		
1 inch	=	2.54 centimeters
1 centimeter	=	0.39 inches
1 foot	=	0.3 meters
1 meter	=	3.3 feet
1 mile	=	1.6 kilometers
1 kilometer	=	0.62 miles
degrees F	=	(degrees C x 1.8) + 32
degrees C	=	(degrees F - 32) x 0.56

Fahrenheit	Celsius
212	100
176	80
140	60
104	40
68	20
32	0
−4	−20
−40	−40

Remember, it is easier to make any necessary conversions within one system first, and then convert the value to that of the other system. For example, instead of trying to remember that there are 39,370 inches in a kilometer, it would be easier to convert 39,370 inches to miles, and then convert miles to kilometers. Such a problem would work like this:

A distance of 200,000 inches equals a distance of how many kilometers?

200,000 inches equals 3.16 miles (200,000 inches / 63,360 inches per mile).

3.16 miles equals 5.06 kilometers (3.16 miles x 1.6 kilometers per mile).

So, 200,000 inches equals 5.1 kilometers.

And here is an example of a temperature conversion, too:

A temperature of 75º Fahrenheit is equal to what temperature Celsius?

75ºF - 32 = 43

43 x 0.56 = 24.08ºC

So, a temperature of 75º Fahrenheit is equal to a temperature of 24.1º Celsius.

Complete the following sentences, rounding figures to the nearest tenth:

20) A distance of 1,500 feet equals a distance of _____450_____ meters.

21) A distance of 6,500 meters equals a distance of __21,450__ feet.

22) There are ____9,900____ feet in 3 kilometers.

23) A distance of 8 miles equals a distance of ____12.8____ kilometers.

4

24) A distance of 53 kilometers equals a distance of ___33.1___ miles.

25) A temperature of 90º Fahrenheit is equal to a temperature of _32.5°_ Celsius.

26) A temperature of 40º Fahrenheit is equal to a temperature of _~~32.22~~ 4.5°_ Celsius.

27) A temperature of 10º Celsius is equal to a temperature of __50°__ Fahrenheit.

28) A temperature of 45º Celsius is equal to a temperature of __113°__ Fahrenheit.

Part VI

The *density* of a material, gas, or object, etc. is a measure of how much mass a given volume of it would have. In the U.S. Customary system it is oftentimes given as pounds per cubic foot, which is the number of pounds that a cubic foot of a material would weigh, with a cubic foot being a sample with dimensions of one foot by one foot by one foot. Likewise, in the metric system density is typically measured as grams per cubic centimeter (abbreviated as cm^3 or cc). Thus, density is given as the number of grams that a cubic centimeter of a material would weigh, with a cubic centimeter being a sample with dimensions of one centimeter by one centimeter by one centimeter.

For example, a container of water having a volume of 1 cubic centimeter ($1cm^3$) would weigh approximately 1 gram (plus the weight of the container). So, the density of water can be given as $1g/cm^3$.

$1cm^3$ of water is 1 gram

With this in mind, note that it is imperative that you understand that an object's density is not related to its size. For example, if a rock sample has a volume of 1 cubic centimeter and has a mass of 3 grams, then its density would be 3g divided by $1cm^3$ = $3g/cm^3$. And, if a 100 cubic centimeter sample of the same type of rock had a mass of 300 grams, its density would be 300g divided by $100cm^3$ = $3g/cm^3$. So, even though the samples are different sizes and have different masses, their densities are the same because they are composed of the same material.

$D = \dfrac{m}{v}$

Using the equation Density = Mass/Volume, complete the following sentences:

29) If a sample of water has a volume of $300cm^3$, then its mass would be __300g__ and its density would be __$1g/cm^3$__ .

30) Seawater has salt dissolved in it, so a $1cm^3$ sample of normal seawater would have a mass of 1.026g rather than 1g, and its density would thus be _____ ← $1.026g/1gcm^3$

31) If a $100cm^3$ sample of Styrofoam has a mass of 10g, then its density would be only $10g/100cm^3$.

32) If an oak log has a volume of $30,000cm^3$ and a mass of 24kg (convert to grams), then its density would be $24,000g/30,000cm^3$ $24kg = 24,000g$

33) Granite has an average density of $2.7g/cm^3$, so a $200cm^3$ sample would have a mass of __540g__ .

$2.7g/cm^3 = \dfrac{m}{200cm^3}$ $2.7 \times 200 = 540g$

34) If a sample of lead has a density of $11.3g/cm^3$ and a mass of 500g, its volume would be $44.2cm^3$.

$11.3g/cm = \dfrac{500g}{v}$

35) Gold is very soft when pure. So, most gold jewelry is only 1/2 (12 carat) to 2/3 (18ct) gold, which is mixed with other metals to make it stronger. Pure gold is exceptionally dense too, as a pure gold (24ct) necklace with a volume of $14cm^3$ and a mass of 270g would have a density of $19.3g/cm^3$

$\dfrac{270}{14} = 19.3$

5

Lab 2: Earth-Sun Relations

You've probably noticed that the days in the summer are longer than the days in the winter. However, you may not have noticed that the Sun rises higher in the sky in the summer, too. In this lab exercise we'll look at these seasonal changes, and you'll learn how the length of days and how high the Sun will rise in the sky changes at different times of the year at different locations.

Objectives:

1) Learn to identify the solstices/equinoxes, and the dates on which they occur.

2) Learn the length of days (from sunrise to sunset) on the solstices/equinoxes at various locations.

3) Learn where the Sun can be seen directly overhead on the solstices/equinoxes.

4) Learn how to determine the Sun's maximum altitude at various locations on the solstices/equinoxes.

Part I

Using the diagrams on page 7, for the Northern Hemisphere (NH), what solstice/equinox is represented by each of the lettered positions and about what date will it occur on?

A) Summer solstice, on/about June 21

B) FALL   Septer 21

C) WINTER   Dec

D) SPRING   March

Using the diagrams on page 7, how long will the days be for each of the numbered positions? Note that all answers should be either 24 hours, 12 hours, or 0 hours.

1) 24   4) 12   7) 0   10) 12

2) 12   5) 12   8) 12   11) 12

3) 0   6) 12   9) 24   12) 12

Complete the following sentences:

13) If the first day of Northern Hemisphere summer is on/about ___June 21st___, then the first day of winter, which is 6 months later, must be on/about ___December 21st___.

14) If the first day of Northern Hemisphere spring is on/about ___March 21st___, then the first day of fall, which is 6 months later, must be about ___September 21st___.

15) If the North Pole has 24 hours of daylight in the summer, it must have ___0___ hours of daylight in the winter, and must also have ___12___ hours of daylight in both the spring and fall.

16) If the South Pole has a 24 hours of daylight on December 21st, then the North Pole must have a ___0___ hours of daylight on December 21st.

17) Since the Equator is right between the North Pole and the South Pole, it must have ___12___ hours of daylight every day of the year.

18) If ___December 21___ is the first day of summer in the Southern Hemisphere, then it must be the first day of ___Winter___ in the Northern Hemisphere.

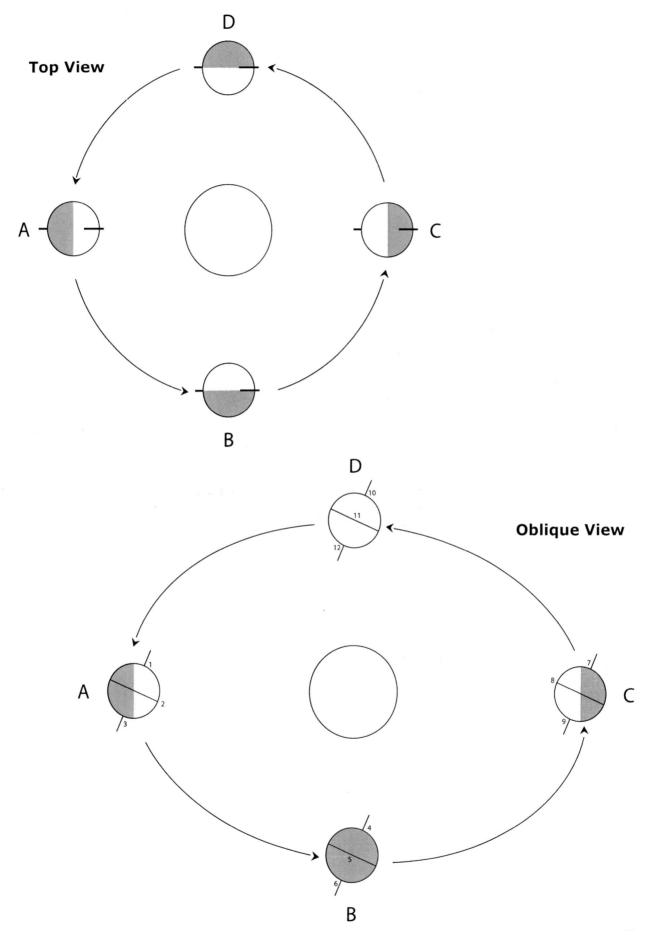

Top View

Oblique View

A

B

C

D

7

Part II

As mentioned earlier, the Sun rises up to different heights in the sky at different times of the year, and this height is properly called its *altitude*, which is given in degrees. Note that if the Sun is on the horizon its altitude is 0°, and if it is straight up in the sky its altitude is 90°. Thus, an altitude of 45° would be right in the middle, or half-way up in the sky. Also note that the altitude can never be more than 90°, as the Sun can never be higher in the sky than straight up.

In this part of the lab you need to determine where you would have to be on the solstices/equinoxes in order to see the Sun straight up (at an altitude of 90°). To do so, take a look at the figure below, which shows the Earth on the NH summer solstice.

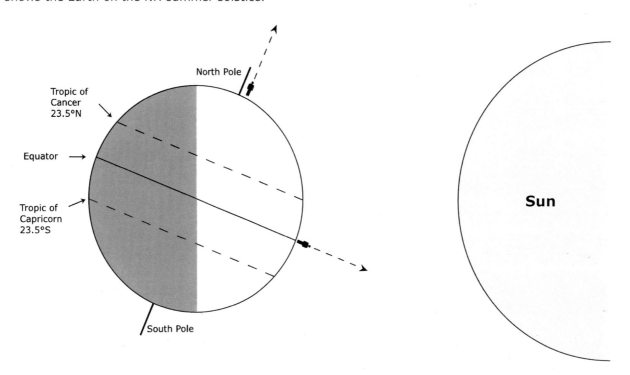

Just imagine being the little person at the North Pole on the figure and think about where the Sun would be in the sky if you stood there for 24 hours. It should be obvious that if you looked straight up the whole time, you would not be looking at the Sun. Instead, it would appear to circle around you, never rising far above the horizon.

Likewise, if you look at the little person standing on the Equator and imagine looking straight up for 24 hours, you still would not be looking right at the Sun at any point. It would appear to be much closer to straight up in the middle of the day than it would be at the North Pole, but it still would not be straight up on the summer solstice.

So, when looking at the picture you should be able to see that you'd have to be standing somewhere in between the North Pole and the Equator if you hoped to see the Sun straight up on the NH summer solstice. But where?

Well, the Earth's axis is tilted 23.5° towards the Sun on the NH summer solstice. Therefore, you'd need to be standing at 23.5°N latitude on that day in order to see the Sun straight up. If it helps you to under-stand this, use a ruler and draw a straight line from the middle of the Sun to the middle of the Earth on the figure. Where does this line intersect the Earth's surface? If you drew the line correctly, it should pass through 23.5°N latitude, otherwise known as the *Tropic of Cancer*. Therefore, if you were to stand on the Tropic of Cancer on June 21st, you would indeed see the Sun straight up in the middle of the day.

To determine where you would have to be on any other dates, just keep in mind that NH winter comes 6 months after NH summer when it is tilted *away from the Sun*, with the equinoxes falling in between.

Complete the following sentences:

19) If the Sun's altitude is __90°__ degrees, it would appear straight up in the sky.

20) If the Sun's altitude is __0°__ degrees, it would appear on the horizon.

21) If you wanted to see the Sun at an altitude of 90º at midday on/about June 21st, you'd have to be standing at __23.5°N__ latitude (*don't forget to use N or S*).

22) If you wanted to see the Sun at an altitude of 90º at midday on/about December 21st, you'd have to be standing at __23.5°S__ latitude.

23) If you wanted to see the Sun at an altitude of 90º at midday on/about March 21st, you'd have to be standing at __0°__ latitude.

24) If you wanted to see the Sun at an altitude of 90º at midday about September 21st, you'd have to be standing at __0°__ latitude.

25) The Tropic of Cancer is at __23.5°N__ latitude, and the Tropic of Capricorn is at __23.5°S__ latitude.

Part III

The highest altitude to which the Sun will rise at a given location and time is called its *maximum altitude*, which is the number of degrees the Sun will rise above the horizon at the mid-point of the day (half-way between sunrise and sunset). In Part II we looked at where the maximum altitude would be 90º on the solstices/equinoxes, but now you need to determine what the Sun's maximum altitude would be for other locations on these dates. We'll use Tampa on the NH summer solstice as an example of how to do this. However, before getting to the mathematical method for determining the Sun's maximum altitude over Tampa, it is best to develop a mental approximation of what the answer should be.

Tampa is at 28ºN latitude, and you previously determined that the Sun would be at 90º altitude over the Tropic of Cancer (23.5ºN) on the NH summer solstice. So, the Sun will be straight up at the Tropic of Cancer, but not over Tampa (it can't be straight up at two locations simultaneously). Still, we are very close to the Tropic of Cancer, where the Sun will be straight up, so the Sun's maximum altitude should be very close to 90º, but not 90º.

With that said, here's how to determine the answer:

Step 1: Determine where the Sun will be directly overhead on the date in question.

Step 2: Determine how many degrees latitude your location is from the answer to Step 1.

Step 3: Subtract the degrees of separation from 90º.

And here's how it would work out for Tampa on June 21st:

Step 1: 23.5ºN

Step 2: 28ºN - 23.5ºN = 4.5º (Tampa is 4.5º latitude away from (north of) the Tropic of Cancer)

Step 3: 90º - 4.5º = 85.5º

Therefore, the Sun's maximum altitude over Tampa on the summer solstice would be 85.5º.

You mentally determined that your answer should be very close to 90º, but not 90º, and the mathematic answer is 85.5º. That sounds reasonable, and of course, it is correct. Students often forget to subtract their answer to Step 2 from 90º, so the most common wrong answer is 4.5º. But, you should be able to see that this cannot be correct. After all, if the Sun's maximum altitude was only 4.5º, it would barely rise above the horizon.

Solve the following problems:

26) What would the Sun's maximum altitude be over Tampa on the winter solstice?

> Hint: Don't forget that on the winter solstice the Sun will be directly overhead at 23.5ºS, not 23.5ºN, so your answer cannot be 85.5º. Instead, there will be a much greater separation between the two locations. On the summer solstice you determined that the Sun's maximum altitude would be close to 90º over Tampa, but on the winter solstice we'd be far from where the Sun is directly overhead. So, your answer should be far from 90º.

Step 1: $23.5°S$

Step 2: $28°N + 23°55S = 51.5°$

Step 3: $90° - 51.5° = 38.5°$

The Sun's maximum altitude over Tampa on the winter solstice would be __38.5__.

27) What would the Sun's maximum altitude be over Tampa on the spring equinox?

Step 1: $0°$

Step 2: $28° - 0° = 28°$

Step 3: $90° - 28° = 62°$

The Sun's maximum altitude over Tampa on the spring equinox would be __62°__.

28) What would the Sun's maximum altitude be over Tampa on the fall equinox?

Step 1: $0°$

Step 2: $28° - 0° = 28°$

Step 3: $90° - 28° = 62°$

The Sun's maximum altitude over Tampa on the fall equinox would be __62°__.

Now try Seattle, Washington, which is at 47ºN latitude.

29) What would the Sun's maximum altitude be over Seattle on the summer solstice?

Step 1: $23.5°N$

Step 2: $47' - 23.5 = 23.5$

Step 3: $90° - 23.5 = 66.5°$

The Sun's maximum altitude over Seattle on the summer solstice would be __66.5°__.

30) What would the Sun's maximum altitude be over Seattle on the winter solstice?

Step 1: $23.5°S$

Step 2: $47 + 23.5°S = 70.5$

Step 3: $90 - 70.5 = 19.5°$

The Sun's maximum altitude over Seattle on the winter solstice would be __19.5°__.

10

31) What would the Sun's maximum altitude be over Seattle on the spring equinox?

Step 1: 0°

Step 2: $41 - 0 = 41$

Step 3: $90 - 41$

The Sun's maximum altitude over Seattle on the spring equinox would be ___43___.

32) What would the Sun's maximum altitude be over Seattle on the fall equinox?

Step 1: 0°

Step 2:

Step 3:

The Sun's maximum altitude over Seattle on the fall equinox would be ___43___.

Lastly, let's look at a location that's even further north. Try Barrow, Alaska which is at about 70ºN.

33) What would the Sun's maximum altitude be over Barrow on the summer solstice?

Step 1: 23.5^oN

Step 2: $70^o - 23.5 = 46.5$

Step 3:

The Sun's maximum altitude over Barrow on the summer solstice would be _____.

34) What would the Sun's maximum altitude be over Barrow on the winter solstice?

Step 1:

Step 2:

Step 3:

The Sun's maximum altitude over Barrow on the winter solstice would be _____.

35) What would the Sun's maximum altitude be over Barrow on the fall equinox?

Step 1:

Step 2:

Step 3:

The Sun's maximum altitude over Barrow on the fall equinox would be _____.

LAB 3: Humidity

Humidity is defined as the amount of water vapor (gaseous water) present in a parcel of air. It can be expressed in several ways, and you'll become familiar with two of these in this lab exercise. You'll also learn how to use a simple device to measure relative humidity, look at how/why humidity changes under different circumstances, and how it relates to and affects various phenomena.

Objectives:

1) Learn how to determine the specific humidity of a parcel of air.

2) Learn about the relationship between air temperature and water vapor capacity.

3) Learn to determine the relative humidity of a parcel of air.

4) Learn to use a sling psychrometer to determine the relative humidity of a parcel of air.

5) Learn about how/why humidity changes under different circumstances.

6) Learn how humidity relates to and affects various phenomena.

Part I

How it's done is unimportant, but it is possible to extract essentially all of the water vapor from a given parcel (sample) of air. If you begin with a parcel of air that has a known mass, say 1 kilogram, and then weighed the water vapor extracted from the sample, then you could easily calculate the specific humidity of that air. *Specific humidity* is simply the humidity expressed as a mass of water in a mass of air.

For example, if a box contains 1 kilogram of air and you find that there are 20 grams of water vapor in the box, then the specific humidity of the air in the box would be 20 grams per kilogram (20g/kg). Like-wise, if a box contains 5 kilograms of air and there are 100 grams of water vapor in the box, then the specific humidity of the air in the box would still be 20g/kg, since each kilogram of air would still hold 20 grams of water vapor.

So, as you can see, to calculate the specific humidity of a parcel of air, you simply divide the mass of water vapor present by the mass of air the parcel contains.

Specific Humidity = grams of water vapor present / kilograms of air present

Complete the following sentences: $20 / 4 \quad 5 / 1$

1) A box holding 1 kilogram of air contains 4 grams of water vapor, so the specific humidity of the air in the box is ___4g/Kg___. (don't forget to use g/kg with specific humidity).

$12g/4kg$

2) A box holding 4 kilograms of air contains 12 grams of water vapor, so the specific humidity of the air in the box is ___3g/Kg___.

$25g/5kg$

3) A box holding 5 kilograms of air contains 25 grams of water vapor, so the specific humidity of the air in the box is ___5g/kg___.

4) A box holding 3 kilograms of air with a specific humidity of 9g/kg must contain ___27___ grams of water vapor.

5) A box holding 6 kilograms of air with a specific humidity of 2g/kg must contain ___12___ grams of water vapor.

12

Part II

Any given parcel of air can hold only so much water vapor, as it simply isn't possible to endlessly add more, and more, and more water vapor to it. At some point the air would become saturated and no more water vapor could be added. The amount of water vapor that the air can hold is dependent upon on the air's temperature, too.

As the temperature of any parcel of air rises, so does its *water vapor capacity* (the amount of water vapor it can hold). Likewise, if a parcel of air cools, then its water vapor capacity falls. So, warm air can hold more water vapor than cold air, and the difference in capacity is quite significant. For example, a box holding 1 kilogram of air would also be able to hold 5 grams of water vapor if the temperature was 5°C (pretty cold), while the same box would be able to hold 47 grams of water vapor if the temperature was 40°C (hot).

See the table to the right, and keep in mind that you do not need to learn it, but do need to know how to read it and understand what the information on it represents. It will also be used in Part III.

Air Temperature	W.V. Capacity
40°C	47g/kg
30°C	28g/kg
25°C	20g/kg
20°C	14g/kg
15°C	10g/kg
10°C	7g/kg
5°C	5g/kg
0°C	3.5g/kg
-10°C	2g/kg
-20°C	0.75g/kg
-30°C	0.3g/kg
-40°C	0.1g/kg

Complete the following sentences:

6) If a parcel of air has a temperature of -10°C, it would be able to hold __*2*__ grams of water vapor per kilogram of air.

7) If a parcel of air has a temperature of 30°C, it would be able to hold __*28*__ grams of water vapor per kilogram of air.

8) If a parcel of air is heated, its water vapor capacity will go __*up*__.

9) If a parcel of air is cooled, its water vapor capacity will go __*down*__.

10) If a parcel of air is heated from 10°C to 20°C, its water vapor capacity will rise from __*7g/kg*__ to __*14g/kg*__. (don't forget to use g/kg when expressing the capacity).

11) If a parcel of air is cooled from 40°C to 0°C, its water vapor capacity would fall from __*47g/kg*__ to __*3.5g/kg*__.

Part III

Humidity can also be expressed as a percentage that indicates how close a given parcel of air is to being saturated. For example, if a box is holding 1 kilogram of air at 15°C, then its capacity would be 10 grams of water vapor. But, what if it actually contains 5 grams of water vapor? Then the *relative humidity* would be 50%, as it would contain half the water vapor needed to saturate it. It's the same as saying the kilogram of air in the box is holding 50% of the water vapor that it could possibly hold. Likewise, if a box contained 2 grams of water vapor, but could hold as much as 6 grams of water vapor, then the relative humidity would be 33% since it would contain one third of the water vapor needed to saturate it.

Instead of dealing with fractions and conversions to percentages, you can calculate the relative humidity by dividing the grams of water vapor present by the grams of water vapor required to saturate the air present, and then multiplying the answer by 100. Put another way, this would be dividing "what you have" by "what you could have" then multiplying by 100.

R.H. = (grams of water vapor present / grams required to saturate the air present) X 100

Still, when calculating relative humidity, it's always a good idea to mentally determine an approximate answer before coming up with a mathematic one, and there's an easy way to do this. Here's an example:

If a box holding 1 kilogram of air has a temperature of 30°C, the water vapor capacity would be 28g/kg (found on the table on the previous page). If this parcel is actually holding 25g of water vapor, then it is very close to saturation. So, it has a high relative humidity.

On the other hand, if the air in the box has a capacity of 28g/kg but is actually holding 5g of water vapor, then is very far from saturation. So, the relative humidity is very low. Or, if the air in the box has a capacity of 28g/kg but is actually holding 13g of water vapor, then it is about half way since 13 is pretty close to half of 28. So, the relative humidity is close to 50%.

Basically, if the two numbers are close to each other the relative humidity will be high, and if they're far apart from each other the relative humidity will be low. Anything else falls in the middle, of course. Thus, you should be able to come up with a rough idea of what the relative humidity is before actually doing any calculations.

We're still not done though, as it's important to note that relative humidity is strongly affected by any changes in temperature, since the water vapor capacity of air changes when the temperature changes. This was not the case for specific humidity, since a change in temperature doesn't actually add or take away water vapor, it simply changes how much could *potentially* be held. So, here are a couple of examples of how temperature changes can affect relative humidity:

If a box contains 1kg of air at a temperature of 25°C, then its capacity is 20g/kg (again, from the table on the previous page). If it actually contains 10g of water vapor, then its relative humidity is 50%, since it is holding exactly one half of the water vapor needed to saturate the air in the box.

However, if the air in the box is heated to 30°C, then the capacity rises to 28g/kg. It would still be holding 10g though, so the air would be *further from saturation* even though the amount of water vapor stayed at 10g. Now the relative humidity would be about 36% instead of 50%.

On the other hand, if the air in the box is cooled to 20°C, then the capacity falls to 14g/kg. It would still be holding 10g though, so the air would be *closer to saturation* even though the amount of water vapor still stayed at 10g. Now the relative humidity would be about 71% instead of 50%.

So, you need to remember: If the amount of water vapor present stays the same but the temperature rises, then the capacity rises, making the relative humidity fall. Conversely, if the amount of water vapor present stays the same but the temperature falls, then the capacity falls, making the relative humidity rise.

Complete the following sentences, rounding to the nearest whole percent:

4okg

12) If a parcel of air has a capacity of 10g/kg and is holding 5g/kg, the relative humidity would be
___50%___ (don't forget to use a percent sign with relative humidity).

13) If a parcel of air has a capacity of 10g/kg and is holding 1g/kg, the RH would be __10%__.

14) If a parcel of air has a capacity of 15g/kg and is holding 13g/kg, the RH would be __87%__.

15) If a parcel of air has a temperature of 10°C and a specific humidity of 5g/kg, its capacity would be
__7g/kg__ and the RH would be __71__

16) If a parcel of air has a temperature of 30°C and a specific humidity of 5g/kg, its capacity would be
__28g__ and the RH would be __18%__.

(What you have/what you Could have) x 100

14

Part IV

Devices used to measure the humidity of air are called *hygrometers*, and in this part of the lab you'll learn how to use a simple hygrometer, along with a table, to determine the relative humidity at various locations on campus.

The hygrometer we'll use is called a *sling psychrometer*, and is very easy to operate. It consists of two thermometers, one that's called the *dry bulb thermometer*, while the other, which has a small cotton wick on the end of it, is called the *wet bulb thermometer*. Both of these thermometers are mounted on a frame that can be spun around by holding a handle that's attached to it by a swivel.

The wick on the wet bulb thermometer is wetted with water just before use, and the psychrometer is then spun around for about 2 minutes. During this time some of the water on the wick will evaporate, and this evaporation cools off the wet bulb thermometer. If the air is relatively dry there will be significant evaporation leading to significant cooling, but if the air is relatively humid there will be much less evaporation and cooling. However, the dry bulb thermometer will stay the same temperature regardless of the humidity.

After spinning the device, the wet bulb temperature is subtracted from the dry bulb temperature. This difference between the two readings is called the *depression of the wet bulb*, which is how many degrees it went down from the starting temperature. Then, the temperature of the dry bulb and the depression of the wet bulb are used along with a *psychrometric table* (next page) to determine the relative humidity.

To determine the relative humidity, go down the left side of the psychrometric table to find the dry bulb temperature, then go across the table until you find the relative humidity value lined up under the depression of the wet bulb at the top of the table.

Before trying, think first! If the temperature of the wet bulb ends up staying close to the temperature of the dry bulb, then there wasn't much cooling. If there wasn't much cooling, then there wasn't much evaporation. And, if there wasn't much evaporation, then the relative humidity must be high. So, a small depression of the wet bulb means the relative humidity is high.

Conversely, if the temperature of the wet bulb drops well below the temperature of the dry bulb, then there was a lot of cooling. If there was a lot of cooling, then there was a lot of evaporation. And, if there was a lot of evaporation, then the relative humidity must be low. So, a large depression of the wet bulb means the relative humidity is low.

Using the psychrometric table on the next page, complete the following sentences:

17) When using a sling psychrometer, if the dry bulb reads 40ºC and the wet bulb reads 30ºC, the depression of the wet bulb would be __10°C__.

18) When using a sling psychrometer, if the dry bulb reads 35ºC and the wet bulb reads 30ºC, the depression of the wet bulb would be __5°C__.

19) When using a sling psychrometer, if the dry bulb reads 30ºC and the wet bulb reads 20ºC, the relative humidity would be __39./__ (don't forget to use a percent sign).

20) When using a sling psychrometer, if the dry bulb reads 36ºC and the wet bulb reads 33ºC, the relative humidity would be __81%__.

21) When using a sling psychrometer, if the dry bulb reads 20ºC and the wet bulb reads 20ºC, the relative humidity would be __100%__.

Psychrometric Table
Depression of W.B. (°C)

D.B. (°C)	1	2	3	4	5	6	7	8	9	10	11	12	13	14	15	16	17	18
0°	81	63	45	28	11													
2°	83	67	51	36	20	6												
4°	85	70	56	42	27	14	3											
6°	86	72	59	46	35	22	10											
8°	87	74	62	51	39	28	17	6										
10°	88	76	65	54	43	38	24	13	4									
12°	88	78	67	57	48	38	28	19	10	2								
14°	89	79	69	60	50	41	33	25	16	8	1							
16°	90	80	71	62	54	45	37	29	21	14	7	1						
18°	91	81	72	64	56	48	40	33	26	19	12	6	0					
20°	91	82	74	66	58	51	44	36	30	23	17	11	5	0				
22°	92	83	75	68	60	53	46	40	33	27	21	15	10	4	0			
24°	92	84	76	69	62	55	49	42	36	30	25	20	14	9	4	0		
26°	92	85	77	70	64	57	51	45	39	34	28	23	18	13	9	5		
28°	93	86	78	71	65	59	53	45	42	36	31	26	21	17	12	8	4	
30°	93	86	79	72	66	61	55	49	44	39	34	29	25	20	16	12	8	4
32°	93	86	80	73	68	62	56	51	46	41	36	32	27	22	19	14	11	8
34°	93	86	81	74	69	63	58	52	48	43	38	34	30	26	22	18	14	11
36°	94	87	81	75	69	64	59	54	50	44	40	36	32	28	24	21	17	13
38°	94	87	82	76	70	66	60	55	51	46	42	38	34	30	26	23	20	16
40°	94	89	82	76	71	67	61	57	52	48	44	40	36	33	29	25	22	19

Relative Humidity (%)

Class Exercise:

	D.B. Temperature (°C)	W.B. Temperature (°C)	Depression of W.B. (°C)	Relative Humidity (%)
Classroom 1	24	19	5	62%
Classroom 2	23	18	5	61%
Hallway	26	22	4	70%
Outdoors	33	31	2	86%
Men's Room	26	23	3	77%
Women's Room	26	24	2	85%

Part V

Now let's apply some of the information from this lab to a variety of real-life situations. As you'll see, there are many day-to-day phenomena that you've probably seen and experienced, which can be easily understood if you have a good knowledge of how humidity works.

Answer the following questions: humidity

22) Does a dehumidifier change the specific humidity in a room? Why?

Yes, Since Specific is the about of water vapor is in the air.

23) Does a dehumidifier change the relative humidity in a room? Why?

Yes, it takes Water vapor out of the air.

24) If you turn on a heater in your home or car, what effect does it have on the specific humidity? Why?

No, Since it does not add or take any humidity in the room

25) If you turn on a heater in your home or car, what effect does it have on the relative humidity? Why?

If you turn on a heater the capacity goes up, but the water stays the same

26) If you turn on an air conditioner in your home or car, what effect does it have on the relative humidity? Why?

It cools the room so the capa.

27) Why does water condense on a cold glass of water or soda, etc.?

28) Why does water typically condense on the windows in a room if it gets cold outside at night?

29) Why is it possible to "see your breath" in the winter, but not in the summer?

30) Why does a hair dryer dry your hair?

31) Why does a "dry heat", like they have in Arizona, feel so much better than the "hot and humid" conditions we have here?

LAB 4: Air Masses, Fronts, and Weather Maps

Weather maps of some sort or another can be seen on TV, online, and on weather apps, etc. However, many people have little to no knowledge of the data and various symbols shown on them, despite the fact that many are easy to identify and understand. So, in this lab exercise you'll become familiar with air masses, fronts, and various types of weather maps.

Objectives:

1) Learn the types of air masses and the symbols that represent them.

2) Learn the different types of fronts and the symbols that represent them.

3) Learn to identify air masses and fronts on weather maps.

4) Learn to develop wind directions/circulation from a pressure pattern on a weather map.

5) Learn to correlate precipitation and cloud phenomena to pressure patterns and fronts.

Part I

Air masses are large parcels of air that develop over land or water and move across Earth's surface. Those that develop over land are typically relatively dry and called *continental air masses* (c), while those that develop over water are typically relatively humid and are called *maritime air masses* (m). These may also form at high or low latitudes, with those forming at high latitudes being relatively cold and called *polar air masses* (P), while those that form at low latitudes are relatively warm and are called *tropical air masses* (T). Thus, we have four basic types of air mass, cP, cT, mP, and mT, with each type having different characteristics.

Complete the following sentences:

1) A _Continental-Polar_ air mass is abbreviated as cP, and the air within it is relatively _dry_ and _cold_.

2) A _Continental-Tropical_ air mass is abbreviated as cT, and the air within it is relatively _dry_ and _warm_.

3) A _Maritime-Polar_ air mass is abbreviated as mP, and the air within it is relatively _humid_ and _cold_.

4) A _Maritime-Tropical_ air mass is abbreviated as mT, and the air within it is relatively _humid_ and _warm_.

Part II

When two air masses come into contact, the boundary between them is called a *front*, and the location where this boundary intersects the ground is marked with an appropriate symbol on weather maps. There are four types of fronts, with each having its own symbol.

When a relatively warm air mass runs into a relatively cool air mass we call the boundary between them a *warm front*, and these are marked by a red line with red half-circles drawn on one side of it, pointing in the direction of motion. On the other hand, when a relatively cool air mass runs into a relatively warm air mass we call it a *cold front*, and these are marked by a blue line with blue triangles drawn on one side of it, again pointing in the direction of motion.

At other times, a warm air mass and a cool air mass may move past each other rather than run into each other, and this is called a *stationary front* since the boundary between the two is relatively stationary. These are marked with an alternating red and blue line, with red half-circles on the red part, pointing towards the cool air mass, and blue triangles on the blue part, pointing towards the warm air mass.

Lastly, when a more complicated interaction occurs in weather systems called *mid-latitude cyclones*, a stationary front may begin to rotate so that cool air pushes under warm air, which rises over cool air (this will be explained further in the lecture). When this happens, an *occluded front* develops, which is marked by a purple line with alternating purple half-circles and triangles on the same side, all pointing in the direction of rotation.

Draw each type of front below, and write what color each type is:

5) Cold front:

6) Warm front:

7) Stationary front:

8) Occluded front:

Part III

Weather Map 1 (pg. 21) shows the barometric (air) pressure in millibars, measured at various locations.

9) What is the barometric pressure (in millibars) in the center of the low pressure system?

10) Mark the location of the low pressure system on the map, using a large L.

11) If the Earth didn't spin, air would always move in a straight line from areas of relatively high pressure into areas of lower pressure. Thus, the air would move perpendicular to isobars. However, the Earth does spin, giving rise to the Coriolis Effect, which deflects winds to the right of their direction of travel in the Northern Hemisphere. Because of this, winds typically move at a 30 to 45 degree angle to isobars on land, rather than perpendicular to them. Using this information, draw several arrows on the map showing how the surface winds would cross the isobars in this system.

Part IV

Weather Map 2 (pg. 22) is a radar image of precipitation produced by a weather system. Areas receiving light precipitation are colored dark blue, which grades to red for areas receiving heavy precipitation.

12) Warm fronts tend to produce light to moderate, and often scattered precipitation, but cold fronts typically produce a distinct line of thunderstorms that produce heavy precipitation. Using this information, draw in the frontal boundaries that would fit with the location and severity of the precipitation shown. Be sure to use the proper symbols for the fronts.

Part V

Weather Map 3 (pg. 23) shows areas of high pressure marked with a large blue H, while areas of low pressure are marked with a large red L. It also shows the warm front and cold front produced by this weather system, and boxed areas where tornado watches have been announced.

13) Label which front is which, and take note of how well they match (or don't match) the fronts you drew on Weather Map 2. They should be the same, or at least close to it.

14) What is the probable nature of the air masses in the area marked with a large A, and the area marked with a large B on Weather Map 3, which are meeting where the cold front is shown?

    A:

    B:

15) Write the proper air mass symbols in the area marked with a large A and the area marked with a large B on Weather Map 3 to identify their probable nature.

Part VI

Weather Map 4 (pg. 24) is an infrared satellite image of the same weather system, which shows the clouds present over the U.S.

16) Using the maps that you have already examined, mark the following:

The fronts, using the proper symbols.

The area of lowest pressure, using a large L.

The large scale wind movement, using several arrows showing circulation.

17) Using these maps to see the nature of the weather system, what would this type of large scale system be called?

Note: Weather Maps 3 and 4 must be completed and turned in with the quiz covering this lab.

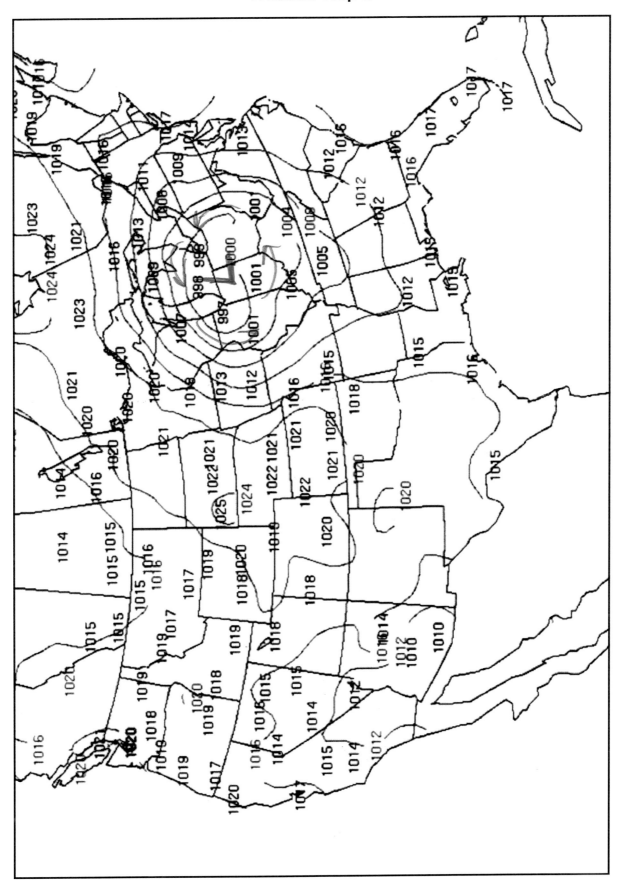

Weather Map 2

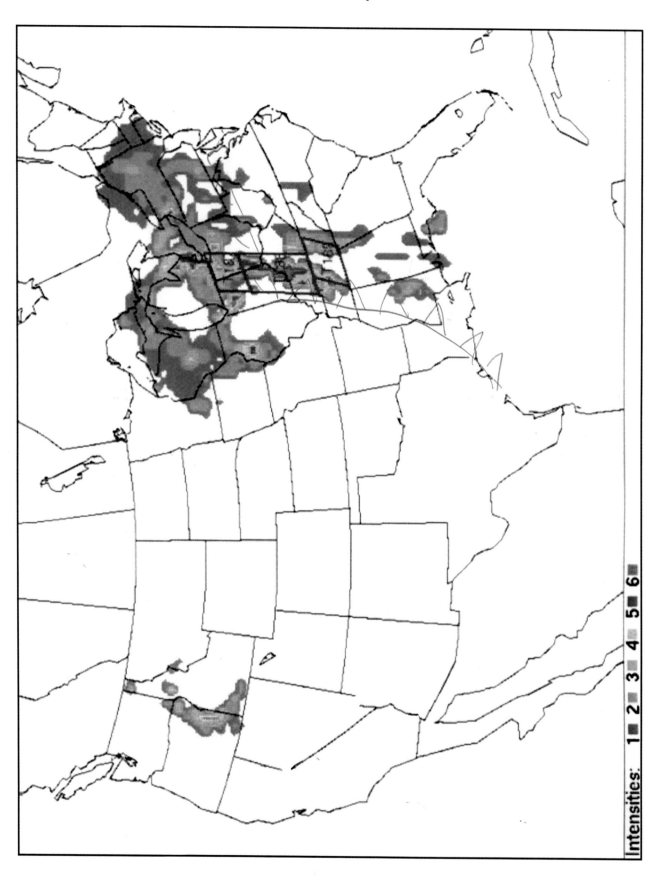

Intensities: 1 2 3 4 5 6

22

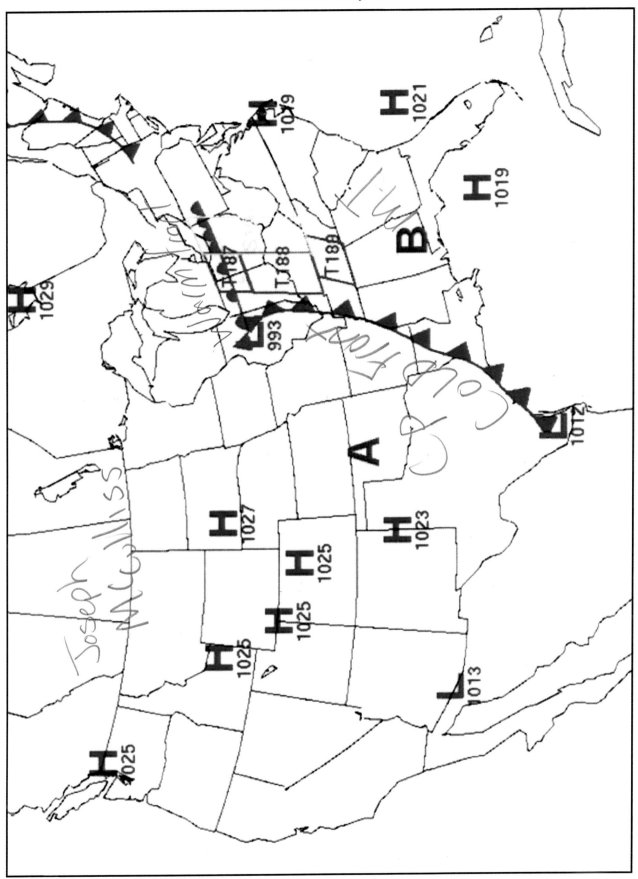

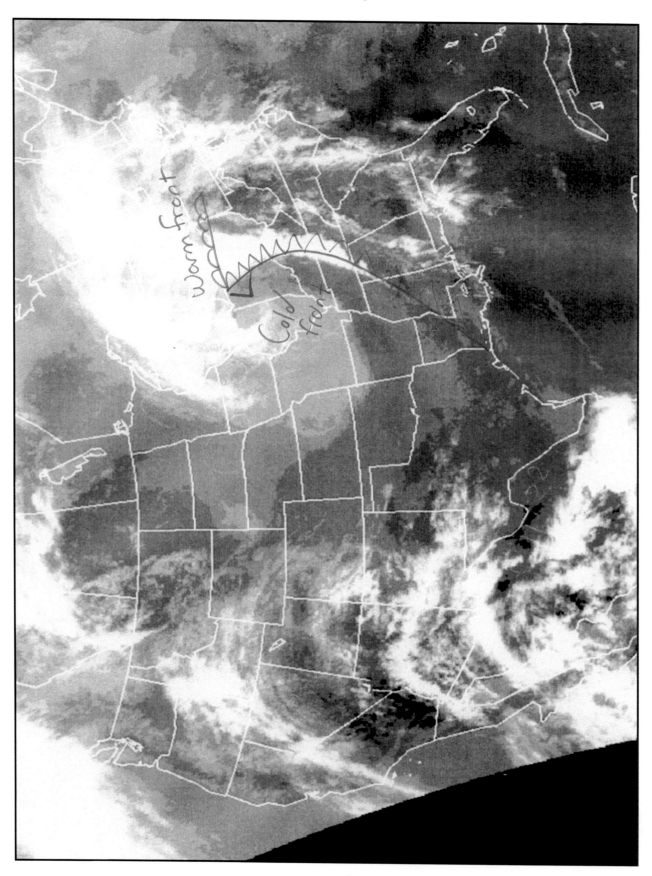

LAB 5: Severe Weather

Severe weather is considered to be any dangerous meteorological phenomenon with the potential to cause property damage, serious social disruption, and/or threaten human health. It's most commonly in the form of thunderstorms, tornados, and tropical cyclones (called hurricanes in the U.S.), which you'll learn more about in this lab exercise.

Objectives:

1) Learn the stages of the life of a cumulonimbus storm cloud, and how to determine the approximate distance to a thunderstorm.

2) Learn how tornadoes are ranked, when they typically occur, and how their potential for destruction varies with wind speed.

3) Learn the types of tropical cyclonic weather phenomena, how tropical cyclones are ranked, when and where tropical cyclones typically develop, and the types of damage they can cause.

Part I

1) The "life" of a cumulonimbus storm cloud has three stages, which are the cumulus stage, mature stage, and dissipating stage. In the boxes below, make rough sketches of each of the three stages and use several arrows to show the updrafts and downdrafts that occur within the cloud during each stage.

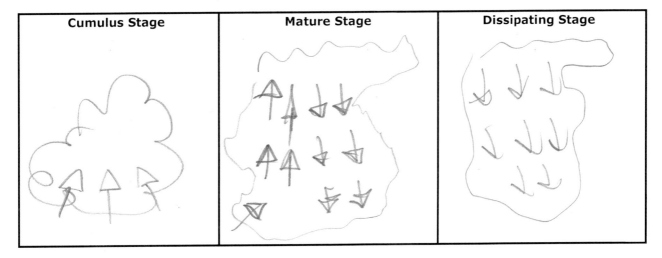

Cumulus Stage	Mature Stage	Dissipating Stage

Part II

Light travels so fast (about 671,000,000mph) that the flash of light from a bolt of lightning reaches an observer almost instantaneously. However, sound travels much slower (about 770mph), so the thunder produced by a bolt of lightning takes approximately 5 seconds to travel one mile.

Complete the following sentences:

2) If you are 6 miles from a thunderstorm and see a flash of lightning come from it, it would take about __30__ seconds for the thunder to reach you.

3) If you see a flash of lightning coming from a thunderstorm and about 10 seconds pass before you hear thunder, the thunderstorm must be about __2__ miles away.

4) If you see a flash of lightning coming from a thunderstorm and about 25 seconds pass before you hear thunder, the thunderstorm must be about __5__ miles away.

Part III

Tornadoes are intense, rotating wind systems that can have the highest wind speeds of any weather phenomenon. In fact, the most powerful tornadoes have had measured wind speeds of over 300mph, which can cause great destruction.

Answer the following questions:

5) On what scale are tornadoes ranked?

Enhanced fujita Scale

6) What is this scale based upon?

Wind Speed

7) What time of the year do the most tornadoes occur in the United States?

late spring early summer months

As wind moves faster and faster, the amount of force it can exert on an object increases as the square of the increase in its velocity. For example, if a 25mph wind hits an object with X amount of force, wind moving twice as fast, at 50mph, would hit the same object with a force of 4X rather than 2X. This is calculated by determining the increase in wind velocity, and then squaring the increase.

In a given situation the increase in wind velocity is determined by dividing the higher wind speed by the lower wind speed. Then, this increase is squared (multiplied by itself).

Complete the following sentences:

8) If a thunderstorm produces a strong gust of wind moving at 50mph, it hits a house with a given amount of force. If a small EF-1 tornado formed and hit the same house with 100mph winds, it would hit the house with _____ times as much force.

9) If the same tornado intensified to an EF-4 and hit another house with 200mph winds, it would hit the house with _____ times as much force as a 50mph wind!

10) If the same tornado continued to intensify to an EF-5 and hit another house with 300mph winds, it would hit the house with _____ times as much force as a 50mph wind!!!

Part IV

Tropical cyclones that we call hurricanes are also intense, rotating weather systems that can cause severe *wind damage*, *inland flooding from heavy rainfall*, and *coastal flooding due to storm surge*. These begin their development as low pressure systems over warm water, called tropical depressions, which may intensify to tropical storms if atmospheric pressure continues to fall. In situations where atmospheric pressure falls even further and wind speeds correspondingly increase, strong rotation develops and a hurricane is formed.

Answer the following questions:

11) If the maximum sustained wind speed produced by a tropical cyclonic weather system ranges from 0 to 38 miles per hour, what is the system called?

12) If the maximum sustained wind speed produced by a tropical cyclonic weather system ranges from 39 to 73 miles per hour, what is the system called?

13) If the maximum sustained wind speed produced by a tropical cyclonic weather system is 74 miles per hour or higher, what is the system called in the United States? What would it be called in Japan?

14) On what scale are hurricanes ranked?

15) What is this scale based upon?

16) When are hurricanes most likely to form in the Atlantic/Caribbean/Gulf of Mexico region? In other words, when is our "hurricane season"?

17) Again, what are the three basic types of damage that can be caused by a hurricane?

18) Historically, which of the above has caused the greatest damage and loss of life?

19) On the map below, mark the areas where tropical cyclones are likely to develop.

20) Also on the map below, mark the areas where the names hurricane, typhoon, and cyclone are used.

21) Lastly, on the map below, mark the most common tracks that tropical cyclones follow.

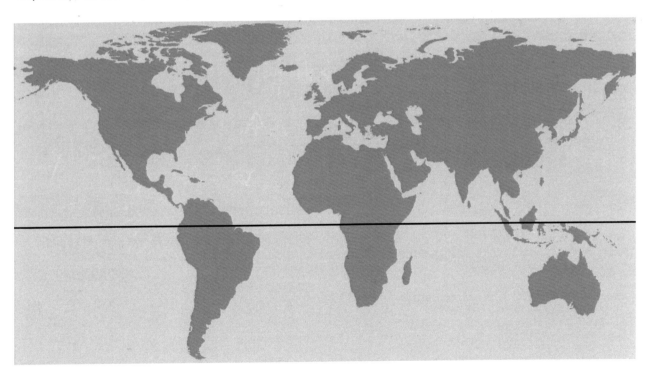

LAB 6: Topographic Maps Pt.1

Despite the increasing availability and decreasing cost of electronic navigation systems, the ability to read a map is a good skill to have. In this lab and the following two, you will develop your basic map reading skills, focusing on United States Geological Survey topographic maps, in particular. These specialized maps show roads and other man-made structures, but also show elevations and other information typically absent from most maps.

Objectives:

1) Learn the basic features of a topographic map.

2) Learn how to interpret contour lines on a topographic map.

3) Learn how to determine the elevation of locations and structures using a topographic map.

Part I

A U.S.G.S. *topographic map* includes the basic features found on other types of maps, including roads major bodies of water, and other notable natural and man-made structures. However, a topographic map also includes many other features, including a map name and number, an edition number, detailed orientation information, all bodies of water, all man-made structures, contour lines that indicate elevations, various scales of distance, and more. You need to know how to identify these and use contour lines, so some information about each is given below.

BRANDON, FL

1999

NIMA 4539 IV NE-SERIES V847

Each different U.S.G.S. topographic map has a specific name and number assigned to it, and also has an edition number that indicates the last update of the map. This is important, as features (especially man-made features) change over time, and a user should typically get information from the most recent version of a given map.

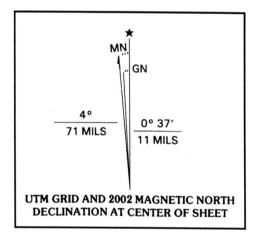

UTM GRID AND 2002 MAGNETIC NORTH DECLINATION AT CENTER OF SHEET

Each map also includes orientation information that indicates which direction is north. It is important to note that there are two indicators though, one being grid north and the other being magnetic north. Grid north indicates which direction north is in relation to lines of longitude, which go from pole to pole. However, the Earth acts something like a giant magnet, but the magnetic field is slightly offset from the actual poles, which are the points on the Earth's surface that correlate to its axis of rotation. In other words, a magnetic compass doesn't actually point to the poles at the axis of rotation. So, the difference in grid north and magnetic north is indicated, allowing a compass user to determine which direction is grid north.

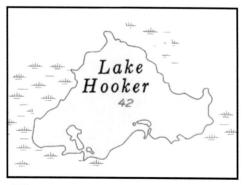

All natural and man-made bodies of water are shown and are colored blue, while all man-made houses, buildings, and such are shown in black. Roads are variable in color though, as smaller ones are usually black, but larger roads like highways and interstates have their own symbols and colors, often including red. Other structures may also be shown, and many maps include a legend, or key, that indicates what each map symbol represents.

Topographic maps also include brown contour lines that indicate the approximate or exact elevation of a location above sea level. These lines are based on surveys, aerial photographs, and satellite data, and can be used by a map reader to determine the elevation of any feature on a map, and also see the terrain of the area on the map. These will be covered in detail in Part II.

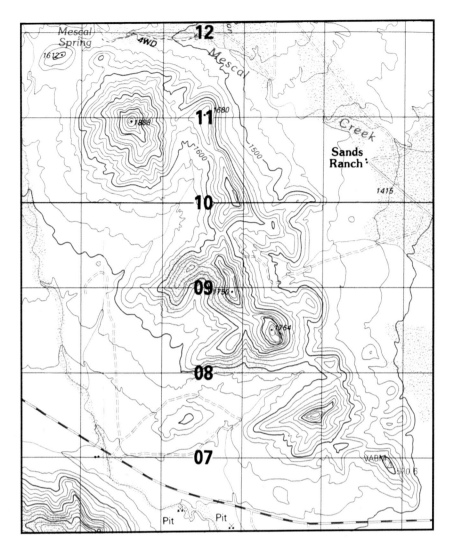

Lastly, each map also includes a number of scales that can be used to determine the distance between locations/features, including graphic scales and a representative fraction scale (like those shown below). These will be covered in detail in Lab 7.

SCALE 1:24 000

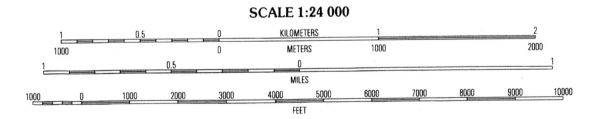

Part II

Topographic maps include *contour lines*, which join locations of equal elevation. The easiest way to think about how these work is to imagine a survey crew determining the elevation of numerous locations in an area and then "connecting the dots" between the locations that all have the same elevation by using brown lines. Thus, if a line is used to connect two points on a map that have the same elevation, any point on that line should be quite close to the elevation of the two connected points.

The fact that these lines connect areas of equal elevation also means that the terrain of an area can be seen, such as hills, valleys, slopes, and such. An easy way to think about how this works is to again imagine a survey crew painting a line all the way around the bottom of a hill at 10' above sea level, then another line around at 20', and another at 30', etc. Looking at the two pictures below it is easy to see that this would end up looking much like a bull's eye from above. Of course, real hills are seldom perfectly round, but the pattern of lines that would be produced around a hill of any shape could still be viewed from above and would indicate the shape and elevation of the hill.

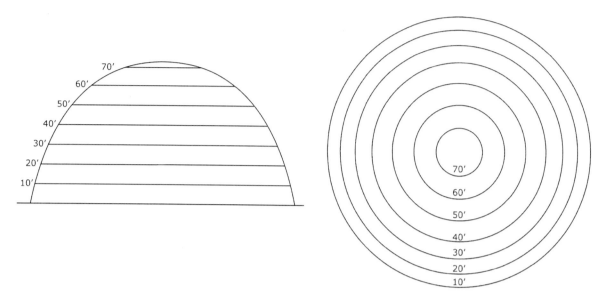

It is also important to note that the vertical distance between contour lines can vary from map to map. This distance is called the *contour interval*, and it is chosen according to the terrain in a given area. This is because it would not make much sense to use a contour line for every 10 feet of vertical change on a map of the Himalaya Mountains, as the map would be covered by thousands of brown lines. Likewise, it wouldn't make sense to use a contour line for every 10 feet of vertical change on a map of the Great Plains, as the map may not have any lines at all, since every location on the map might be within 10 feet of elevation of each other.

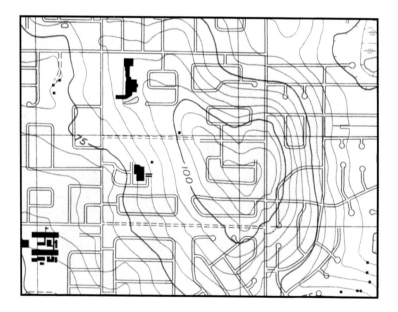

Lastly, it is also important to note that every contour line does not have an elevation written on (within) it. Typically, a map will have a heavy contour line with an elevation written within it, then four light contour lines without elevations written within them, then another heavy contour line with an elevation written within it, etc. Thus, knowing the contour interval is critical, and it is typically indicated at the bottom-center of a map. See the picture to the left for an example.

Part III

If a location/structure is on a contour line, then its elevation is easy to determine as it will be the same as the contour line. However, there are other things to note when determining the elevation of a location or structure that is not on a contour line.

To start, there are many times when a location/structure's elevation has been surveyed and is indicated by a benchmark, which is typically shown as an X or the letters BM with an elevation next to it. Elevations are sometimes shown at the surface of bodies of water and hill/mountain tops, too. However, when an unsurveyed location/structure is between contour lines, there is a specific procedure for indicating its elevation.

In such cases, a location/structure that sits between contour lines should be given an elevation that indicates that its exact elevation is unknown, but is between two known elevations. This is done by using the elevation of the lower of the closest contour lines and adding half of the contour interval to it, followed by +/- half of the contour interval. This is easiest to understand by looking at the example below:

The contour interval for this example is 10 feet, and a building is between the 70' and 80' contour lines. So, its elevation must be higher than 70 feet and lower than 80 feet. Its exact elevation isn't known though, so you should add ½ of the contour interval to 70, and follow this with +/- half of the contour interval. Therefore, its elevation is 75' +/- 5' (70' + 5' +/- 5') Yes, this is a fancy way of indicating that the building is somewhere between 70 and 80 feet above sea level.

The same technique is also used for any body of water that does not have its elevation indicated. For example, if the contour interval of a map is 10 feet and the closest contour line to the edge of a lake is 50 feet, then the surface of the lake must be lower than 50 feet, but must also be higher than 40 feet. So, its elevation would be 45' +/- 5' (40' + 5' +/- 5').

Lastly, at times there may be features on a map that can be confused with hills, but are actually depressions (such as sinkholes). In such cases, the contour lines around the depression will be marked with downward-pointing tick marks (hachure marks) to alleviate any confusion. See the picture to the right for an example:

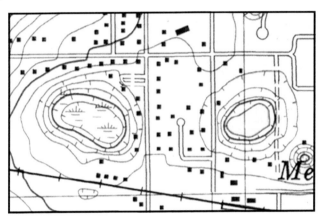

Using the map on page 32, complete the following sentences:

Note: the contour interval is 5 feet.

1) The building at point A is _____50_____ feet above sea level.

2) The building at point B is _____40_____ feet above sea level.

3) The building at point C is _____60_____ feet above sea level.

4) The building at point D is __47.5 ± 2.5__ feet above sea level.

5) The school at point E is __42.5 +/- 2.5__ feet above sea level (use the dot in the middle of the circle).

6) The elevation of the intersection at point F is __47.5 +/- 2.5__ feet above sea level.

7) The elevation of the surface of Wee Lake at point G is __32.5 +/- 2.5__ feet above sea level.

8) The elevation of the surface of the pond at point H is __~~37~~ 32.5 +/- 2.5__ feet above sea level.

9) The elevation of the surface of Chapman Lake at point I is _____35_____ feet above sea level.

10) The elevation of the top of the hill at point J is __87.5 +/- 2.5__ feet above sea level.

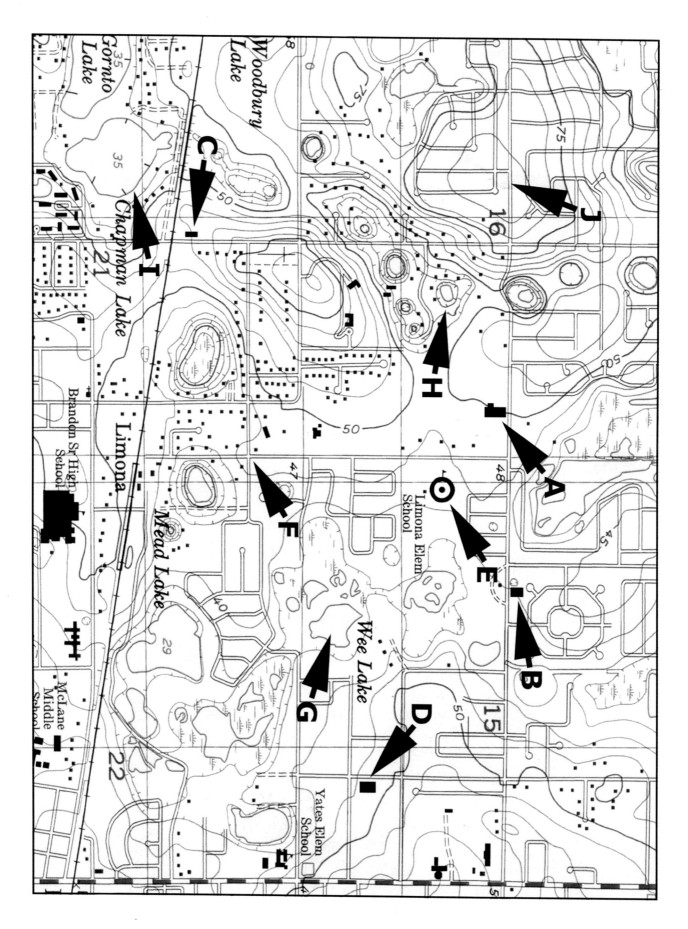

LAB 7: Topographic Maps Pt.2

In this continuation, we will again work with topographic maps, specifically determining distances.

Objectives:

1) Learn the different scales used on a topographic map.

2) Learn how to determine distances on a topographic map.

Part I

U.S.G.S. topographic maps typically have two types of scales. Usually there are multiple *graphic scales* and a single *representative fraction scale*, all of which can be used to determine the ground distances between points on the map.

Graphic scales, which are often called bar scales, can be used quite easily as they are picture-type scales that are comprised of bars of a specific length related to distances on the map. No calculations or rulers are required to use them. An example can be seen below:

SCALE 1:24 000

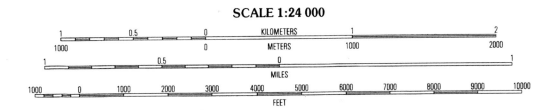

A representative fraction scale (often called an R.F. scale and typically located above the graphic scales) is quite different though, as it is a single ratio that indicates that one unit of measure on the map is equal to a specified number of the same units in ground distance. For example, an R.F. scale of 1:10000 indicates that if two points on a map are 1 inch apart when measured with a ruler, then those two points are actually 10,000 inches apart in ground distance. Likewise, if the R.F. scale was 1:50000, and the distance between two points was 3 inches when measured with a ruler, then the two points would actually be 150,000 inches apart in ground distance (3" x 50000 = 150,000").

It is very important to remember that there are no specified units, though. So, a map user can use any unit of measurement they choose, as long as the units are kept the same on both sides of the ratio. In other words, you could measure the distance between two points in centimeters and use the scale to determine the number of centimeters between those two points in ground distance, or in inches to determine the number of inches between those two points in ground distance, or even in feet to determine the number of feet between those two points in ground distance (if it was a very large map). Therefore, it is up to you to choose the most appropriate unit of measure.

Part II

Using a piece of string or paper, or a ruler, along with a graphic scale to determine distances is quite simple, and the technique for doing so will be demonstrated by the instructor. However, using the R.F. scale is typically a more involved (but not difficult) process, and three examples are provided below:

In this example we want to find the ground distance between the road intersections at points A and B on the section of a U.S.G.S. topographic map on page 36 in feet, miles, meters, and kilometers by using an R.F. scale of 1:24000, which is commonly used with U.S.G.S. topographic maps.

To determine the distance between these two intersections in feet, the first step is to measure the map distance between them in inches. Since they are 5.25 inches apart and the scale is 1:24000, then the actual ground distance between them is 126,000 inches (5.25" x 24000 = 126,000").

From there, the inches of ground distance must be converted to feet. This is done by dividing the ground distance by 12, since there are 12 inches in a foot. Therefore, the ground distance between the intersections is 10,500 feet (126,000" / 12 = 10,500').

Continuing on, to determine the distance between the intersections in miles, the same initial steps are taken to determine the ground distance between them in inches (126,000"). However, instead of dividing by 12 to convert this distance to feet, the number of inches should be divided by 63,360, since there are that many inches in a mile. Therefore, the ground distance between the intersections is approximately 2 miles (126,000" / 63,360 = 1.99 miles).

Next, to determine the distance between the two intersections in meters, the first step is to measure the distance between them in centimeters (to stay within the metric system). Since they are 13.3 centimeters apart and the scale is 1:24000, then the ground distance between them is 319,200 centimeters (13.3cm x 24000 = 319,200cm).

From there, the centimeters of ground distance must be converted to meters. This is done by dividing the ground distance by 100, since there are 100 centimeters in a meter. Therefore, the ground distance between the intersections is 3,192 meters (319,200cm / 100 = 3,192m).

Lastly, to determine the distance between them in kilometers, the same initial steps are taken to determine the ground distance between them in centimeters (319,200cm). However, instead of dividing by 100 to convert this distance to meters, the number of centimeters must be divided by 100,000 since there are that many centimeters in a kilometer. Therefore, the ground distance between the intersections is approximately 3.2 kilometers (319,200cm / 100,000 = 3.192km).

Using the map on page 36, with an R.F. scale of 1:24000, complete the following sentences, rounding figures to the nearest tenth (distances should be determined following the roads):

1) The distance from the intersection at Point A to the intersection at Point B is _____ inches.

2) The distance from the intersection at Point A to the intersection at Point B is _____ feet.

3) The distance from the intersection at Point A to the intersection at Point B is _____ miles.

4) The distance from the intersection at Point A to the intersection at Point C (by passing through the intersection at point B) is _____ miles.

5) The distance from the intersection at Point A to the intersection at Point B is _____ centimeters.

6) The distance from the intersection at Point A to the intersection at Point B is _____ meters.

7) The distance from the intersection at Point A to the intersection at Point B is _____ kilometers.

8) The ground distance from the intersection at Point A to the intersection at Point C (by passing through the intersection at point B) is _____ km.

Using the map on page 37, with an R.F. scale of 1:24000, complete the following sentences, rounding figures to the nearest tenth (distances should be determined following the roads):

9) The distance from the intersection at Point A to the intersection at Point B is _____ inches.

10) The distance from the intersection at Point A to the intersection at Point B is _____ miles.

11) The distance from the intersection at Point A to the intersection at Point B is _____ centimeters.

12) The distance from the intersection at Point A to the intersection at Point B is _____ kilometers.

13) When using the curved road west of the interstate, the distance from the intersection at Point C to the intersection at Point D is _____ inches.

14) When using the curved road west of the interstate, the distance from the intersection at Point C to the intersection at Point D is _____ miles.

15) When using the curved road west of the interstate, the distance from the intersection at Point C to the intersection at Point D is _____ centimeters.

16) When using the curved road west of the interstate, the distance from the intersection at Point C to the intersection at Point D is _____ kilometers.

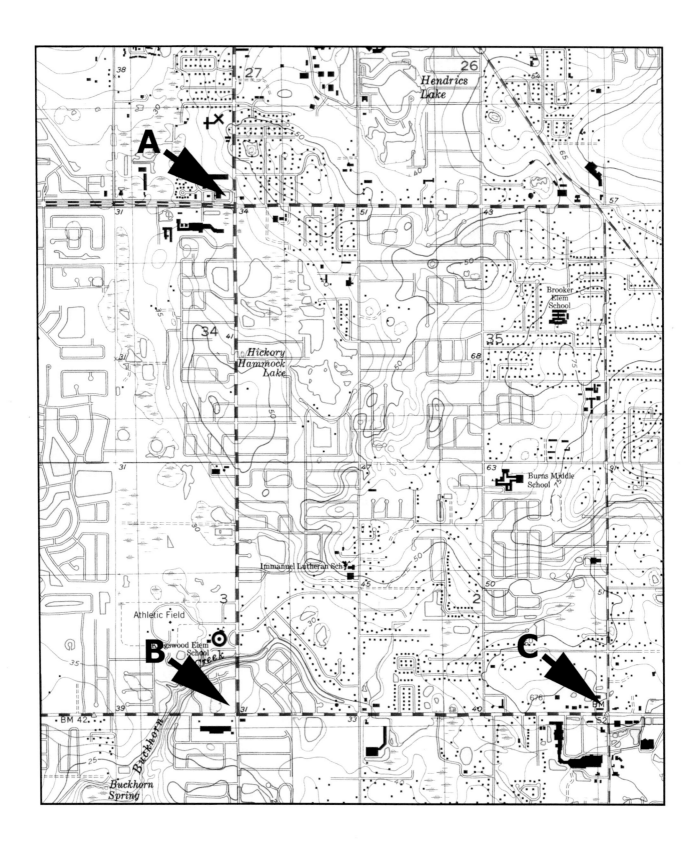

36

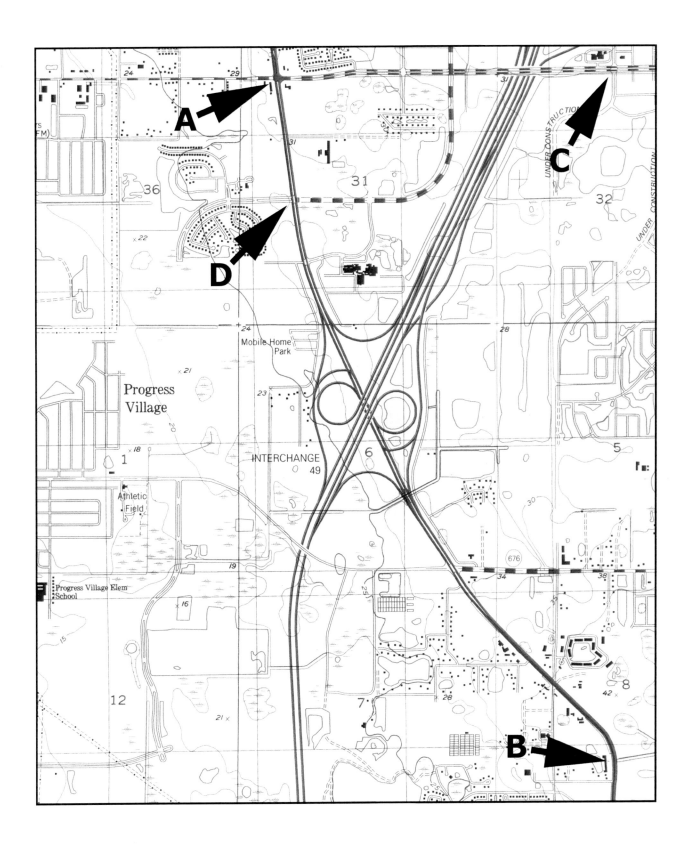

LAB 8: Topographic Maps Pt.3

In this continuation, we will again work with topographic maps, specifically coordinate systems.

Objectives:

1) Learn how to use the longitude and latitude coordinate system.

2) Learn how to use the Public Land Survey System, commonly called the Township and Range system.

Part I

The latitude/longitude coordinate system is used for global navigation and positioning, and can also be found on U.S.G.S. topographic maps. *Latitude* is used to identify a position north or south of the Equator, and *longitude* is used to identify a position east or west of the Prime Meridian, which is an imaginary line that runs from the poles through Greenwich, England (near London). Both are easy to understand with some explanation.

Latitude correlates to the angle of a position north or south of the Equator, which is considered to be 0° latitude. So, the North Pole and South Pole are 90° North and 90° South latitude, respectively. This is because a line drawn perpendicular to the plane of the Equator at the center of the Earth intersects the Earth's surface at each pole. For any other position, its angle above or below the Equator is its latitude. So, all points on the Earth are between 0° and 90° latitude, and an "N" or "S" is usually included with the angle to indicate whether it is north or south of the Equator.

Longitude, on the other hand, correlates to the angle of a position east or west of the Prime Meridian, which is considered to be 0° longitude. So, a line drawn straight though the Earth from the Principal Meridian can be either 180° East or 180° West, and a line drawn perpendicular to this line, through the center of the Earth, is either 90° East or 90° West where it intersects the Earth's surface. For any other position, its angle from Principal Meridian is its longitude. Note that all points on the Earth are between 0° and 180° degrees longitude, and that an "E" or "W" is usually included with the angle to indicate whether it is east or west of the Principal Meridian.

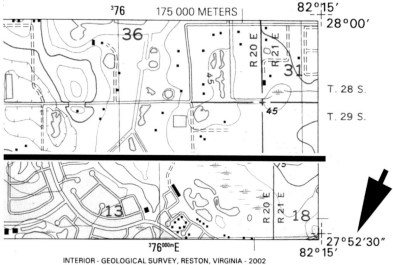

BRANDON QUADRANGLE
FLORIDA-HILLSBOROUGH CO.
7.5-MINUTE SERIES (TOPOGRAPHIC)

INTERIOR - GEOLOGICAL SURVEY, RESTON, VIRGINIA - 2002

Lastly, while it might seem to be more complicated than it should be, degrees of latitude and longitude can be treated like hours that are subdivided into minutes, and to seconds. For each degree of either, there are 60 minutes, and each of these can be sub-divided into 60 seconds. For example, a position exactly between 40°N and 41°N would be at 40°30'N, since 30 minutes is the same as half an hour. Likewise, a position between 40°N and 41°N and 2/3 up from 40°N would be at 40°40'N, since 40 minutes is 2/3 of an hour. From there, the minutes can be sub-divided into seconds the same way. Therefore, a position that is exactly between 40°30'N and 40°31'N would be 40°30'30"N, since 30 seconds is half a minute. See the picture to the left showing the corners of a U.S.G.S. topographic map for some examples, where the arrows point.

Complete the following sentences:

1) If a map has 82°15′ at the top right corner and the same number at the bottom right corner, these would indicate the _____ (latitude or longitude) of the right edge of the map.

2) If a map has 28°00′ at the top right corner and the same number at the top left corner, these would indicate the _____ (latitude or longitude) of the top edge of the map.

3) If a location is exactly between 42°W and 43°W longitude, its specific longitude is _____.

4) If a location is between 65°N and 66°N, but is only 1/3 of the way up from 65°N latitude, its specific latitude is _____.

5) If a location is exactly between 12°N and 13°N latitude and is also 3/4 of the way from 36°E to 37°E longitude, its specific coordinates would be _____ (latitude) and _____ (longitude).

6) If a location is 2/3 of the way from 72°S to 73°S latitude and is also 1/4 of the way from 56°W to 57°W longitude, its specific coordinates would be _____ (latitude) and _____ (longitude).

Part II

When surveying and identifying parcels of land in the U.S. (particularly when dealing with real estate titles and deeds), the Public Land Survey System is used. Commonly called the Township and Range system, it was originally proposed by Thomas Jefferson as the first mathematically designed national survey system in the world. This system might seem a bit cumbersome at first, but it's easy enough to use once you figure out how it works. To start, each state that uses this system chooses a Baseline that runs east-west and a Principal Meridian that runs north-south through the state. These lines often run through the capitol city of the state and serve as a starting point for the system.

The system is based on a grid of blocks, called Townships, that are 6 miles by 6 miles in dimension. Starting from the intersection of the Principal Meridian and the Baseline, the Townships are numbered sequentially, both north and south of the Baseline. The first row of Townships north of the Baseline are called Township 1 North (T1N), the next row up are Township 2 North (T2N), the next are Township 3 North (T3N), etc. Likewise, the first row of Townships south of the Baseline are Townships 1 South (T1S), the next are Township 2 South (T2S), etc.

The Range numbers work the same way, but they run east-west of the Principal Meridian. So, the first row of Ranges west of the Principal Meridian are Range 1 West (R1W), the next are Range 2 West (R2W), etc., with those east of the Principal Meridian being R1E, R2E, etc. The result is a grid of blocks we simply call Townships even though each block is identified by both a Township number and a Range number in a unique combination. See the figure below to understand this better.

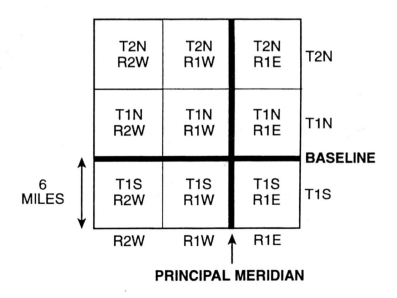

Since each Township is 6 miles by 6 miles in size, each covers 36 square miles (6 mi. x 6 mi. = 36 mi.^{2}). Townships are thus subdivided into 36 Sections, each of which is 1 mile by 1 mile in size, thus covering 1 square mile each. These are numbered 1 through 36, but the numbering is a bit odd. Instead of starting at the top-left of a Township, Section 1 is actually at the top-right. Then they're numbered Section 2, Section 3, Section 4, Section 5, and Section 6 across the top of the Township going from right to left (rather than left to right). The next row down does start from the left though, and is numbered Section 7 though Section 12 from left to right. Then, the next row goes back to right to left, etc. until Section 36 is reached at the bottom-right of the Township.

See the figure of a Township broken into Sections on the right to understand this better.

6	5	4	3	2	1
7	8	9	10	11	12
18	17	16	15	14	13
19	20	21	22	23	24
30	29	28	27	26	25
31	32	33	34	35	36

← 6 MILES →

Each Section is typically subdivided into Quarters of a Section by splitting it into four equal parts. Larger or smaller fractions of a Section may be used, but Quarters are common, and we'll stick with them.

The top-left Quarter of a Section is simply called the Northwest Quarter, while the top-right is the Northeast Quarter, the bottom-left is the Southwest Quarter, and the bottom-right is the Southeast Quarter.

Lastly, each Quarter of a Section is typically subdivided into Quarters of Quarters in the same manner that Sections are subdivided into Quarters. The top-left Quarter of a Quarter is simply called the Northwest Quarter of a Quarter, while the top-right is the Northeast Quarter of a Quarter, the bottom-left is the Southwest Quarter of a Quarter, and the bottom-right is the Southeast Quarter of a Quarter.

See the figure of a Section divided into Quarters and Quarters of Quarters on the right to understand this better.

NW 1/4 of NW 1/4	NE 1/4 of NW 1/4	NW 1/4 of NE 1/4	NE 1/4 of NE 1/4
NW 1/4		**NE 1/4**	
SW 1/4 of NW 1/4	SE 1/4 of NW 1/4	SW 1/4 of NE 1/4	SE 1/4 of NE 1/4
NW 1/4 of SW 1/4	NE 1/4 of SW 1/4	NW 1/4 of SE 1/4	NE 1/4 of SE 1/4
SW 1/4		**SE 1/4**	
SW 1/4 of SW 1/4	SE 1/4 of SW 1/4	SW 1/4 of SE 1/4	SE 1/4 of SE 1/4

← 1 MILE →

When written out, note that a description starts from the smallest part and proceeds though the largest part. So, the Quarter of a Quarter is written first, followed by the Quarter of a Section, then the Section number, with the Township and Range being last. For example, the parcel of land occupying the Northeast Quarter of the Southwest Quarter of Section 30, in Township 9 North, Range 4 West would have the description NE 1/4 of SW 1/4, Sec. 30, T9N, R4W.

Complete the following sentences:

7) Each Township has dimensions of _6miles_ by _6miles_

8) The first Township north of the Baseline, and immediately west of the Principal Meridian would be _T1N, R1W._

9) The third Township south of the Baseline, and immediately east of the Principal Meridian would be _____.

10) There are ___6___ rows of Sections in a Township.

11) Each Section has dimensions of _1mile_ by _1mile_.

12) The Section at the top-left of a Township is Section ___6___.

13) The Section at the bottom-right of a Township is Section ___36___.

14) The diagrams below show a black rectangle somewhere within Township 21 South, Range 14 East. The rectangle is also located in Section _____, in the _____ 1/4 of the _____ 1/4.

15) When written out properly (using quarters of quarters), the location for the rectangle would be:

16) When written out properly (using quarters of quarters), the location for the circle would be:

17) When written out properly (using quarters of quarters), the location for the pentagon would be:

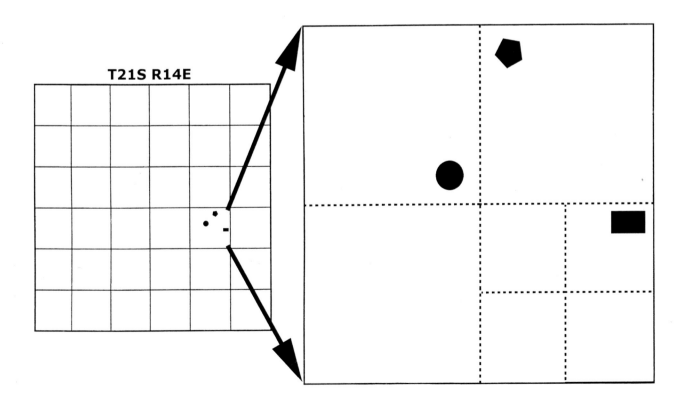

T21S R14E

Lab 9: Minerals and Mineral Identification

In this lab you will learn the basic characteristics of minerals, about the various physical properties of minerals, and how to identify common minerals using an identification key. You will also learn how to identify a few minerals by sight, without the help of a key.

Objectives:

1) Learn the diagnostic properties of minerals.

2) Learn to identify common crystalline minerals by sight.

3) Learn to identify common minerals using an identification key.

Part I

Minerals are naturally occurring inorganic solids with a definite chemical composition and an orderly crystalline structure. There are about 4,000 of them, but each has some particular qualities/properties that make it distinct and identifiable. In this part of the lab you will learn about these qualities/properties and how to utilize them when identifying specimens.

Luster: When trying to identify unknown mineral specimens, generally the first thing to look at is the specimen's luster, which is the appearance of light reflected from its surface. While there are numerous specific types of luster, the broadest division is between those that have a *metallic luster* and those that have a *non-metallic luster*.

Minerals that have a metallic luster look like they are composed of metal. This doesn't simply mean they are shiny though, as some are rather dull, looking more like dark iron. Likewise, a piece of dark-colored glass would not have a metallic luster, as it would be dark and shiny, but still wouldn't look like metal.

Of course, minerals that have a non-metallic luster don't appear to be composed of metal. Some examples of non-metallic lusters are earthy, greasy, pearly, silky, and vitreous, but there are several others. You only need to be concerned with metallic versus non-metallic, though.

Pyrite is a mineral with a metallic luster.

Hornblende is a mineral with a non-metallic luster.

Note that some specimens can be confusing, as there are a few minerals that are composed of metals that have a non-metallic luster and others that aren't composed of metals that do have a metallic luster. However, if a mineral is metallic it will always have a dark streak, whereas a non-metallic mineral will always have a light streak. Streak is covered in more detail on page 44.

Color: At times the specific color of a mineral can be useful when trying to identify it. However, color can also be far less helpful at other times because some minerals may come in a variety of colors, and many different minerals can have the same color. Therefore, it's sometimes better to not rely on specific colors when identifying minerals, but simply to divide non-metallic minerals into those that are light and those that are dark.

Any non-metallic mineral specimen that is black, dark gray, brown, dark green, or dark red is considered to be dark colored, whereas anything else is considered to be light colored. As you'll see on the identification keys, the non-metallic minerals are divided into these two groups

Fluorite is a mineral that can come in many colors.

Hardness: Some minerals are very hard (like diamond), while others are quite soft (like talc), with many more in between (like fluorite). These differences in hardness arise because the bonds holding the atoms together in these minerals have different strengths. So, minerals can be ranked on a ten-point scale called *Mohs Hardness Scale*, which indicates how strongly the atoms are bonded together and how well a specimen can resist being scratched.

Diamond is the hardest mineral (with a hardness of 10), so a sharp piece of diamond would be able to scratch any other mineral, and no other mineral would be able to scratch it. Likewise, talc is the softest mineral (with a hardness of 1), so it can't scratch any other mineral, but all other minerals can scratch it. Everything else falls somewhere on the scale, being able to scratch some minerals, but not others.

You won't be scratching mineral specimens on other specimens, though. Instead, a fingernail, a penny, and a piece of glass will be used to get a rough idea of how hard a specimen is.

A fingernail has a hardness of about 2.5, so anything that will scratch a fingernail must be harder than about 2.5, while anything that won't must be softer than or equal to 2.5. Likewise, a penny (which is coated with copper) has a hardness of about 3.5, and glass has a hardness of about 5.5. So, they can be used the same way, and you will be provided with both of these to use as identification aids.

Mohs Hardness Scale

diamond	10	
quartz	7	
	5.5	glass
fluorite	4	
	3.5	penny
calcite	3	
	2.5	fingernail
talc	1	

Quartz is a mineral with a hardness of 7, so it can scratch glass, which has a hardness of 5.5.

Streak: If you grind a small amount of a mineral specimen into powder, it would seem like the powder should always be the same color as the whole specimen. However, in some cases the powder can be very different in appearance, and this can also be helpful when identifying specimens.

In order to see what a mineral looks like in powdered form, you will use a small ceramic tile called a streak plate. A specimen can be rubbed across this plate, and will leave behind a colored streak, much like a colored pencil would.

Sphalerite is a mineral that is dark in color, but leaves a light-colored (white to yellowish-brown) streak like the one in the picture.

Note that the streak test should only be done for specimens that are opaque (those that do not let any light through), and that you should not attempt to make a streak for specimens that are transparent or translucent. Of course, any mineral that is harder than a streak plate (about 6.5 to 7) won't leave a streak, either.

Crystal Form: When space and plenty of time are available, minerals can oftentimes produce large crystals that have distinct forms. For example, quartz crystals will have six sides and end with a point, while halite crystals will be cube-like with six sides and 90° corners and edges. So, crystal form can sometimes be of use when trying to identify minerals.

However, space/time is often limited and crystals either can't form or are deformed, etc. So, crystal form may not be helpful, as a specimen may not display its characteristic crystal form. Likewise, while there are more than 4,000 minerals, there are only a few unique crystal forms. Thus, many different minerals have the same crystal form.

Different minerals can have different crystal forms. Here you can see quartz and selenite, which are both relatively clear, but have different forms.

Cleavage: Some minerals will break along planes of weakness in their crystalline structure because the chemical bonds that hold the atoms together are stronger in some places than others. If such planes of weakness exist, a mineral is said to have cleavage, meaning it can be cleaved (split) in some fashion.

It can often be difficult to tell if a specimen has cleavage without actually breaking it, but there are times when it can be seen easily. When looking at a transparent or translucent crystalline specimen if there are what appear to be fractures running through it that are parallel to the surface of the crystal, then you are seeing cleavage planes (planes of weakness).

In many cases when minerals have good cleavage it will also appear that a specimen can be broken into smaller pieces that would all have the same overall shape as the original specimen. However, if a mineral does not have cleavage it will break into randomly-shaped pieces that oftentimes having sharp or jagged edges. This is called fracture, and many minerals that lack cleavage display *conchoidal fracture*, meaning they break like glass breaks.

Biotite mica is an example of a mineral that has good cleavage in one direction. It can be easily split into thin sheets.

Reaction with acid: Different acids may affect different minerals. Some minerals can be dissolved by sulfuric acid, but others may be unaffected, while some may be dissolved by hydrochloric acid, etc. Thus, while trying to identify some minerals it can be useful to squirt a few drops of diluted acid on a specimen to see if/how it reacts.

The most common use of acid is to verify whether a specimen is made of calcium carbonate ($CaCO_3$), which *effervesces* (fizzes) when tested with dilute hydrochloric acid. The common minerals calcite and aragonite are both made of calcium carbonate, so both will react with this acid if it is applied to samples of them. Conversely, both halite and quartz, which due to their similar appearances are often mistaken for calcite, will not effervesce.

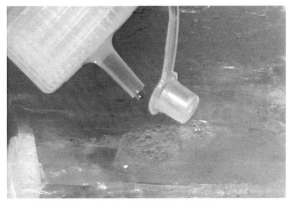

Calcite is a mineral that will effervesce if hydrochloric acid is dropped onto it.

Magnetism: Some iron-containing metallic minerals may be magnetic and/or stick to a magnet. In other words, some would actually pick up a paper clip like a magnet would, while others will only pick up or stick to a magnet. A magnetic mineral will also attract/deflect the needle of a compass.

**If a mineral is magnetic, it can attract/deflect the needle
of a compass, and can pull it away from north.**

Others: There are many other characteristics that can be useful at times, but are rather self-explanatory, or will not be needed for the upcoming exercise. These include characteristics such as taste, feel, smell, elasticity, malleability, fluorescence, and radioactivity. No, you will not have any radioactive specimens, and please refrain from taste testing!

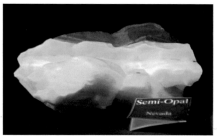

Some minerals and rocks will fluoresce under a black light, looking very different.

Part II

You'll need learn to identify a few common minerals without using a key. These are quartz, calcite, halite, pyrite, and galena, each of which has distinctive properties that can be easily identified by sight.

Complete the following sentences, and be able to identify these five minerals *by sight*:

1) Quartz is usually ___Colorless to white___ in color, often forms ___Six-sided___ crystals, and has ___no___ cleavage.

2) Calcite is usually ___Colorless, white, or yellowish___ in color, often forms ___rhombohedral___ crystals, and has ___good non-cubic___ cleavage. The corners on a crystal have ___75°___ degree angles.

3) Halite is usually ___Colorless to white___ in color, often forms ___Cubic___ crystals, and has ___good cubic___ cleavage. The corners on a crystal have ___90°___ degree angles.

4) Pyrite is usually ___brass-yellow___ in color, and often forms ___Cubic___ crystals. The corners on a crystal have ___90°___ degree angles.

5) Galena is usually ___Silver gray___ in color, and often forms ___Cubic___ crystals. The corners on a crystal have ___90°___ degree angles.

46

Part III

Use the keys below and on page 48 to identify the mineral specimens.

Specimen 1:	HALITE	Specimen 5:	GRAPHITE
Specimen 2:	GALENA	Specimen 6:	PYRITE
Specimen 3:	Quartz	Specimen 7:	CALCITE
Specimen 4:	SPHALERITE	Specimen 8:	MAGNETITE

Mineral Identification Keys

Metallic Minerals

hardness	streak	description	name
6	greenish-black	Brass-yellow. May form cubic crystals with 90° angles.	Pyrite
6	black	Black to dark gray. May be granular. Will attract a magnet or compass needle.	Magnetite
4	greenish-black	Golden-yellow. May tarnish.	Chalcopyrite
2.5	dark gray to black	Silver gray. May form cubic crystals with 90° angles.	Galena
1	dark gray to black	Gray. Will mark paper.	Graphite

Non-metallic minerals are on the next page.

Non-metallic Minerals: Light Color

hardness	description	other	name
7	Colorless, white (milky), pink (rose), or purple (amethyst), and transparent to opaque. Often forms six-sided crystals.	no cleavage	Quartz
4	Colorless, yellow, purple, or green, and transparent to translucent. Often forms cubic crystals with 90° angles.	good cubic cleavage (90°)	Fluorite
3	Colorless, white, or yellowish, and transparent to opaque. Often forms rhombohedral crystals with 75° angles.	good non-cubic cleavage (75°) reacts with acid	Calcite
2.5	Colorless to white, and transparent to opaque. Often forms cubic crystals with 90° angles.	good cubic cleavage (90°) tastes salty	Halite
1 - 2	White, pink, or green, and opaque. Typically has a pearly luster.	feels soapy	Talc

Non-metallic Minerals: Dark Color

hardness	description	other	name
7	Brown or gray to black (smoky quartz), and transparent to opaque. Often forms six-sided crystals.	no cleavage	Quartz
6.5 - 7	Olive green, and transparent to translucent. Often forms small glass-like grains.	no cleavage	Olivine
5 - 6	Black to greenish-black, and opaque. May form rhombohedral crystals.	fair cleavage (60° and 120°)	Hornblende
3.5 - 4	Yellowish-brown to black, and opaque. Often has difficult to determine luster.	streaks white to yellowish-brown	Sphalerite
2.5 - 3	Dark brown to black, and translucent to opaque. Often forms in books of numerous thin sheets.	good cleavage in thin sheets	Biotite

48

Lab 10: Rocks and Rock Identification

In this lab you will learn the basic characteristics of igneous, sedimentary, and metamorphic rocks, and how to identify common rocks using identification keys. You will also develop an understanding of the rock cycle.

Objectives:

1) Learn the diagnostic properties of igneous rocks.

2) Learn to identify common igneous rocks using an identification key.

3) Learn the diagnostic properties of sedimentary rocks.

4) Learn to identify common sedimentary rocks using an identification key.

5) Learn the diagnostic properties of metamorphic rocks.

6) Learn to identify common metamorphic rocks using an identification key.

7) Learn the concept of the rock cycle.

Part I

An igneous rock is any rock that forms when molten rock cools off and solidifies, and they're identified according to their texture and composition. So, it's important for you to know what these textures and compositions are.

Texture: The texture of an igneous rock is simply its overall appearance with regards to the average crystal size it displays and/or the presence of vesicles (bubbles). If molten rock is allowed to cool and solidify very slowly, then large crystals typically form, which are easily visible to the naked eye. On the other hand, if molten rock cools relatively quickly, the crystals will generally be either too small to see with the naked eye, or no crystals will form at all (in the case of exceptionally rapid cooling). So, the majority of igneous rocks either have large crystals and a *coarse grained texture*, small crystals and a *fine grained texture*, or no crystals and a *glassy texture*.

However, there are times when molten rock may solidify at two distinct rates. Imagine magma cooling very slowly underground leading to the formation of some large crystals, but then being ejected during volcanic activity and finishing the crystallization process very quickly, leading to the formation of small crystals. Such a rock would thus have some large (easily visible) crystals that are mixed in a background or matrix of small crystals. This is called a *porphyritic texture*.

Lastly, molten rock may contain large quantities of dissolved gas, which will attempt to escape if brought near or to the surface. If the magma/lava has a sufficiently low viscosity (thickness) and cools slowly enough, these gasses can escape to the atmosphere. However, at other times the gasses cannot escape before crystallization occurs, and the rock produced will contain significant numbers of trapped bubbles. This is called a *vesicular texture*.

Composition: The composition of molten rock is variable for a number of reasons, and igneous rocks may in turn be very light to very dark in overall color.

Granitic igneous rocks, also known as felsic rocks, have a relatively high percentage of light-colored silicate minerals and are relatively high in silica, so they are relatively light in color. There may be significant quantities of dark crystals in such rocks, but their overall appearance is still *light*.

Conversely, basaltic igneous rocks, also known as mafic rocks, contain a relatively high percentage of dark silicate minerals and are relatively low in silica, so they are relatively *dark* in color.

Rocks that have intermediate compositions are also common, and are accordingly *intermediate* in overall color.

Part II

Use the key below to identify the igneous rock specimens.

Specimen 1: *Granite*	Specimen 4: *Rhyolite*
Specimen 2: *Scoria*	Specimen 5: *Diorite*
Specimen 3: *Gabbro*	Specimen 6: *Porphyritic Basalt*

Igneous Rocks			
Texture	**light**	**intermediate**	**dark**
coarse-grained	granite	diorite	gabbro
fine-grained	rhyolite	andesite	basalt
porphyritic	porphyritic rhyolite	porphyritic andesite	porphyritic basalt
vesicular	pumice		scoria
glassy		obsidian	

Part III

A sedimentary rock is any rock made of sediments/chemicals derived from pre-existing rocks, which are classified by their grain size and/or composition. They're split into two categories based on what they're made of, which are *detrital sedimentary rocks* (those made of sediments derived from other rocks) and *chemical sedimentary rocks* (those made of chemicals derived from other rocks). Thus, it's important for you to understand the differences in these and know what grain sizes are and how compositions are used for identification.

Again, detrital sedimentary rocks are made of sediments derived from other rocks, meaning they're made of cemented rock particles derived from pre-existing rocks that have been physically broken down into pieces of gravel, sand, silt, and mud. Such rocks are classified/identified by the average size of the particles that they're comprised of, which is called their *grain size*. Relatively large particles are called *gravel* and are greater than 2mm in size. Rocks made from such particles are said to have a *coarse grain size*. Smaller particles (1/16 to 2mm) are called *sand*, and rocks made from such particles are said to have a *medium grain size*. Even smaller particles (1/256mm to 1/16mm) are called *silt*, and rocks made from such particles are said to have a *fine grain size*. And lastly, even smaller particles (less than 1/256mm) are called *mud*, and rocks made from such particles have a *very fine grain size*.

On the other hand, chemical sedimentary rocks are formed when substances are dissolved away from pre-existing rocks into water and then precipitated from that water to form new rock. This process can occur in a number of different ways, making classification/identification less straightforward. In general they're classified by composition though, both chemical composition and the type of particle(s) they're comprised of.

Many chemical sedimentary rocks are composed of calcite that was produced by various organisms, including shell material, coral skeletons, and plankton skeletons. However, some are made of siliceous plankton skeletons, and plant material. Other chemical sedimentary rocks can be formed abiotically though, meaning their constituents are not produced by living things. These simply precipitate from water under certain conditions, especially when water evaporates and leaves mineral deposits behind.

Part IV

Use the keys below to identify the sedimentary rock specimens. Note that 7-11 are detritral sedimentary rocks, while 12-16 are chemical sedimentary rocks.

Specimen 7: BRECCIA	Specimen 12: COQUINA
Specimen 8: SANDSTONE	Specimen 13: ROCK SALT
Specimen 9: SHALE	Specimen 14: FOSSILIFEROUS LIMESTONE
Specimen 10: CONGLOMERATE	Specimen 15: CHALK
Specimen 11: SILTSTONE	Specimen 16: COAL

Detrital Sedimentary Rocks

Description	Rock Name
coarse grain size = gravel (rounded grains)	conglomerate
coarse grain size = gravel (angular grains)	breccia
medium grain size = sand	sandstone
fine grain size = silt	siltstone
very fine grain size = mud	shale

Chemical Sedimentary Rocks

Description	Rock Name
abiotic calcite	limestone
cemented shells, shell fragments, corals, etc.	fossiliferous limestone
loosely cemented calcitic shells and fragments	coquina
calcitic plankton shells	chalk
siliceous plankton shells and abiotic silica	chert (light) / flint (dark)
halite formed when water evaporates	rock salt
gypsum formed when water evaporates	rock gypsum
compressed and lithified plant matter	coal

Part V

A metamorphic rock is any rock that is formed by the alteration of pre-existing rocks, primarily by the heat and pressure produced by deep burial. The degree of alteration is variable depending on how much heat/pressure a rock is subjected to, so metamorphism can be low-grade to high-grade. When a rock undergoes *low-grade metamorphism* it will typically look much like the original, or *parent*, rock, but *high-grade metamorphism* can alter the appearance of a rock to such a degree that it may look significantly different and bear little resemblance to the parent rock. Regardless, metamorphic rocks are classified/identified based on their texture, grain size, and composition. So, again, it's important for you to understand the differences in these and know what metamorphic textures, grain sizes, and compositions are, and how they're used for identification.

The two metamorphic textures are foliated and non-foliated. *Foliated* metamorphic rocks are produced if any crystals or particles in a rock are re-aligned under high temperature/pressure conditions, which lead to the development of a layered or banded appearance. Conversely, *non-foliated* metamorphic rocks are produced if such crystals/particles do not form layers or bands. This typically occurs when the parent rock is composed of a single mineral.

Grain size, as was the case with the other rock types, is simply the average crystal size of a specimen. Metamorphic rocks can thus be *fine-grained*, *medium-grained*, or *coarse-grained* depending on how large its crystals/particles are.

Lastly, non-foliated metamorphic rocks, which are typically composed of a single mineral, can be further classified by their mineral composition. They are typically made of calcite or quartz.

Part VI

Use the key below to identify the metamorphic rock specimens.

Specimen 17: GNEISS	Specimen 20: SCHIST
Specimen 18: PHYLLITE	Specimen 21: SLATE
Specimen 19: MARBLE	Specimen 22: QUARTZITE

Metamorphic Rocks	
Description	**Rock name**
foliated and very fine grained, looks much like shale	slate
foliated and fine grained, looks like shiny, wavy slate	phyllite
foliated and medium to coarse grained, typically looks scaly or flaky	schist
foliated and medium to coarse grained, has light and dark banding	gneiss
non-foliated and medium to coarse grained, composed of calcite, effervesces with acid, and will not scratch glass	marble
non-foliated and medium to coarse grained, composed of quartz, does not effervesce with acid, but will scratch glass	quartzite

Part VII

Lastly, it is important for you to understand that rocks are continuously recycled and turned into other types of rocks. For example, an igneous rock can be weathered into particles over time, which can then be transported, deposited, and lithified elsewhere to form a sedimentary rock. The sedimentary rock can be buried over time and subjected to intense heat and pressure, thus turning into a metamorphic rock. Then, the metamorphic rock may be heated to such a degree that it melts. If this magma cools off and solidifies, it then produces a new igneous rock, and the cycle can start all over.

Fill in the empty ovals on the diagram below in order to complete the simplified rock cycle.

The Rock Cycle:

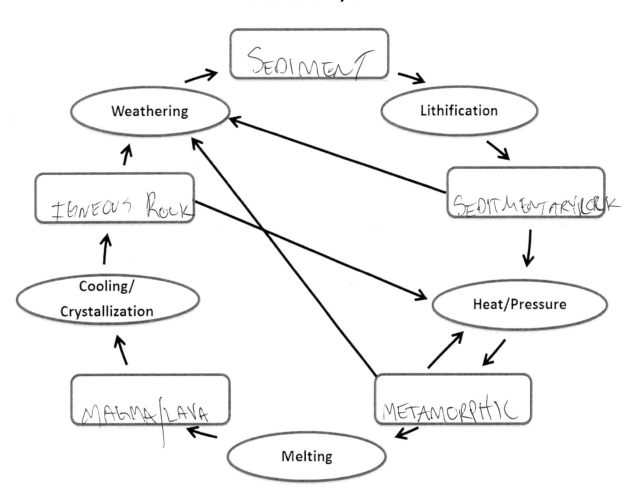

Note that examples of all the rocks covered are presented on the next few pages. Keep in mind that these are only examples though, as all granite does not look exactly like what's shown, nor does all sandstone, or all schist, etc.

Igneous Rocks

gabbro

basalt

porphyritic basalt

scoria

diorite

andesite

porphyritic andesite

obsidian

granite

rhyolite

porphyritic rhyolite

pumice

Detrital Sedimentary Rocks

conglomerate

siltstone

shale

conglomerate

sandstone

shale

breccia

sandstone

55

Chemical Sedimentary Rocks

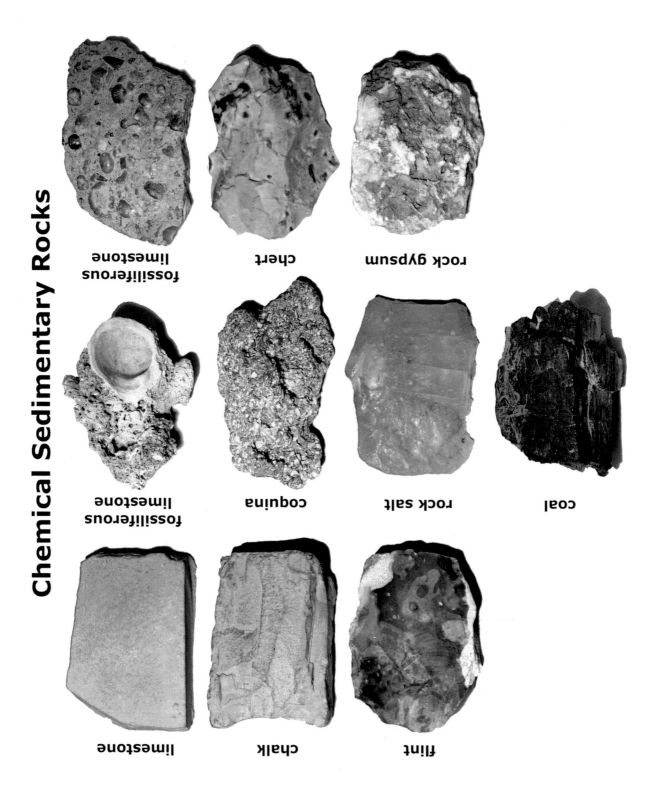

fossiliferous limestone

chert

rock gypsum

fossiliferous limestone

coquina

rock salt

coal

limestone

chalk

flint

56

Foliated Metamorphic Rocks

phyllite

gneiss

phyllite

schist

slate

schist

Non-foliated Metamorphic Rocks

quartzite

marble

57

LAB 11: Streams

Streams are dynamic and are constantly changing over time. Not only do they migrate across the Earth's surface, they can also create a number of distinctive physical features, drastically change the topography of areas, and transport tremendous amounts of sediment and dissolved materials. So, it is important for you to understand how streams "work" and the features associated with them.

Objectives:

1) Learn the basic physical features associated with streams.

2) Learn how to calculate the gradient of a stream.

3) Learn how a stream's gradient and competence are related.

4) Learn how to calculate the competence of a stream.

Part I

Mark the figures below as follows:

1) On the image below, label the cut bank and point bar areas of the stream channel, and the limits of the floodplain.

2) Also, draw an arrow indicating which direction the stream channel is most likely to migrate over time.

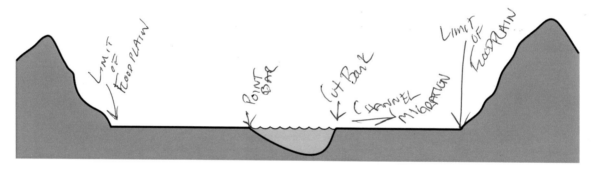

3) On the image below, draw heavy lines to show the limits of the floodplain.

4) Also, circle at least three areas where oxbow lakes are likely to form in the future.

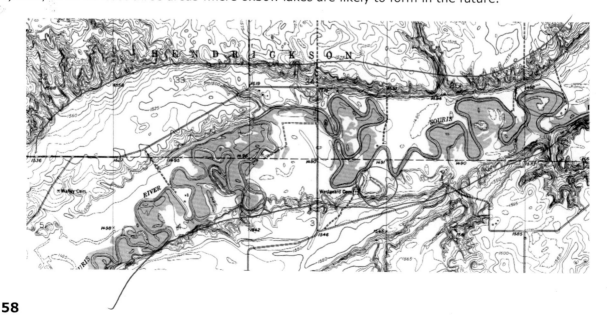

58

Name: Joseph McCulliss

5) On the image below, label all of the cut banks, point bars, and oxbow lakes.

6) Also, draw several arrows indicating which direction each meander is most likely to migrate.

Note: This page and the next must be completed and turned in with the quiz covering this lab.

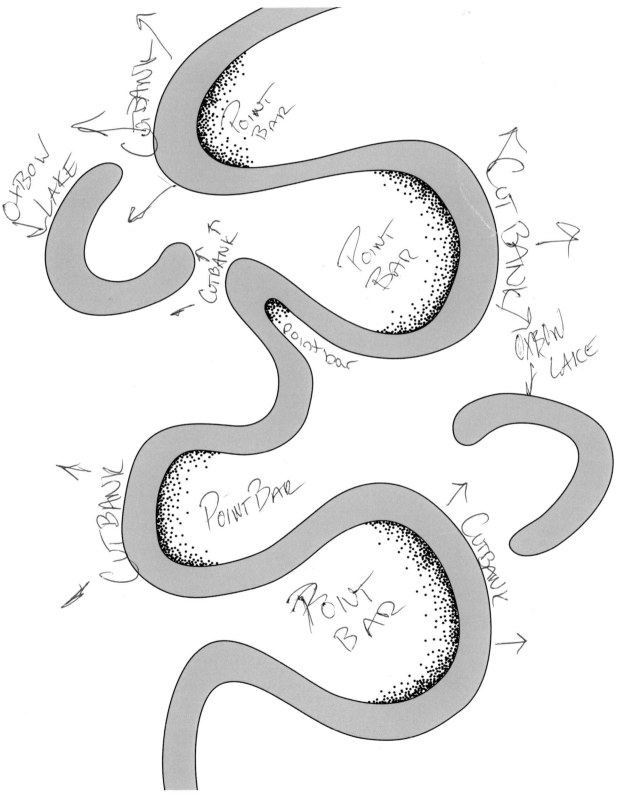

7) On the image below, draw lines/arrows showing where the highest water velocity is found in the stream channel (assuming that flow is from left to right).

8) Also, at the two points marked with arrows, draw a simple sketch showing the expected shape of the stream channel in cross-section.

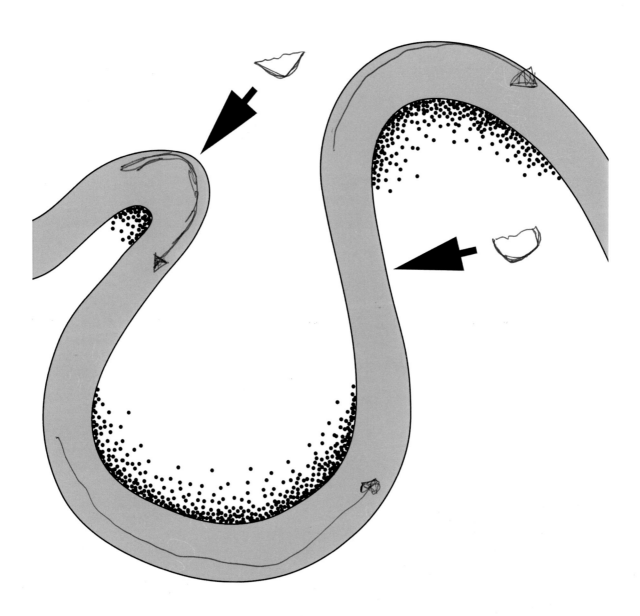

9) On the image below, label the headlands of the stream system, as well as its mouth.

10) Also, label the main meandering channel and the delta produced by the stream system.

11) What type of drainage pattern is shown in the headlands of this stream system?

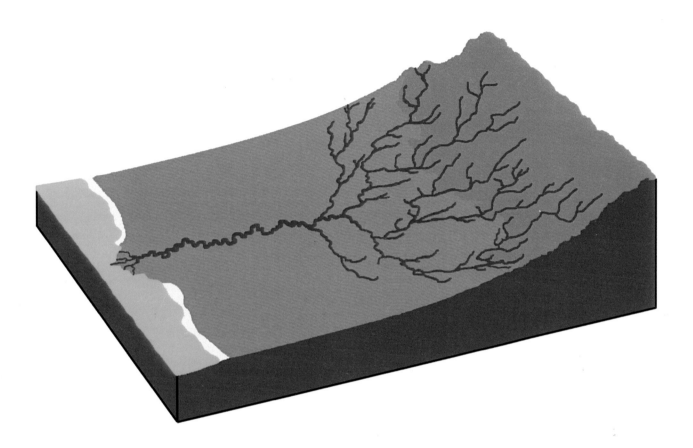

Part II

A stream's *gradient* is its slope expressed as its vertical drop over a specified distance. In other words, it is a number that indicates how much the stream's elevation decreases from one part of the stream to another. So, calculating a stream's gradient is much like a "rise over run" problem from a math course, except that the gradient is often expressed as a fraction with the total change in elevation on top and the total distance traveled on the bottom, which is then simplified.

For example, if a stream channel starts 100 feet above sea level and ends at sea level, its vertical drop is 100 feet, which would go on top. If the distance from the start of the stream channel to the ocean is 10 miles, then 10 miles goes on the bottom. Then the fraction is simplified so that the gradient is expressed as 10 feet per mile, or 10ft/mi. The math would look like this:

100 feet (the starting elevation) - 0 feet (the ending elevation) = 100 feet.

100 feet / 10 miles (the horizontal distance traveled) = 10 feet per mile (or 10ft/mi)

In other words, on average, for every mile of horizontal distance, the stream drops 10 feet.

A stream's gradient can also be expressed as a percent, but there are a couple of extra steps involved. The first thing to do is convert the horizontal distance to the same unit of measure as the vertical drop so that the units on the top and bottom of the fraction are the same. Then divide the top by the bottom, and multiply the result by 100.

The math would look like this:

100 feet (the starting elevation) - 0 feet (the ending elevation) = 100 feet.

10 miles (the horizontal distance traveled) x 5,280 (the number of feet in a mile) = 52,800 feet.

100 feet / 52,800 feet = 0.002

0.002 x 100 = 0.2%

So, the stream's gradient equals 10ft/mi or 0.2%

feet/mile   meter/kilometer

Complete the following sentences:

12) If a stream channel starts at 2,000 feet above sea level and ends at sea level, and covers a distance of 800 miles, the stream's gradient is __2.5 ft/mi__ .

$$\frac{2000}{800 \times 5280} \qquad \frac{2000}{4224000}$$

13) The same stream's gradient would also be __0.05__ percent.

14) If a stream channel starts at 1,200 meters above sea level and ends at sea level, and covers a distance of 400 kilometers, the stream's gradient is __3m/km__ .

$$\frac{1200}{400 \times 1000} \qquad \frac{1200}{400,000}$$

15) The same stream's gradient would also be __0.03__ percent.

16) If a stream channel starts at 4,500 feet above sea level and ends in a lake at 600 feet above sea level, and covers a distance of 400 miles, the stream's gradient is __9.5 ft/mi__ .

$$\frac{0.2}{\quad} \qquad \frac{3900}{400}$$

17) The same stream's gradient would also be __0.2__ percent.

18) If a stream channel starts at 2,200 meters above sea level and ends in a lake at 800 meters above sea level, and covers a distance of 700 kilometers, the stream's gradient is __2m/km__ .

19) The same stream's gradient would also be __0.2__ percent.

Part III

A stream's *competence* is defined as the maximum size particle that it is able to transport. For example, a relatively slow moving stream may be able to transport nothing larger than mud-sized particles and would thus have a very low competence, while a relatively fast moving stream may be able to transport gravel-sized particles and would have a high competence. Of course, this is primarily related to flow velocity, as fast moving water can move larger particles than slow moving water.

This means that if two streams had essentially the same channel size, roughness, and form, but one had a higher gradient than the other, the stream with the higher gradient would have a higher flow velocity and would also have a higher competence. Or, if a stream that normally has a relatively low flow velocity experiences a flood and its flow velocity increases, then its competence will also increase. This should seem simple enough to understand, but the changes in competence that come with an increase in flow velocity can be surprising.

This is due to the fact that if the flow velocity of a stream is doubled, its competence will be four times greater rather than two times greater. Likewise, if its velocity is tripled, then its competence will be nine times greater, etc. In other words, the increase in competence is equal to the increase in flow velocity squared.

For example, if a stream's flow velocity is normally 30cm/sec, but during a flood its velocity increases to 1.2m/sec (120cm/sec), then its flow velocity would be four times greater. This means its competence would be increased 16 times ($4^2 = 16$). So, if it could normally transport relatively small pieces of gravel with masses up to 5 grams, then during floods it would be able to transport pieces of gravel (assuming they are of roughly the same shape and composition) up to 80 grams. Thus, a stream that normally can't move relatively large pieces of gravel can certainly do so during floods.

Complete the following sentences:

20) If a stream can normally transport sand grains with masses up to 1 gram when its flow velocity is 20cm/sec in the winter, it could transport sediments as heavy as _____ if its flow velocity increases to 40cm/sec during a rainy summer.

21) If a stream can normally transport sand grains with masses up to 2 grams when its flow velocity is 20cm/sec, it could transport sediments as heavy as _____ if its flow velocity increases to 80cm/sec during a mild flood.

22) If a stream can normally transport sand grains with masses up to 2 grams when its flow velocity is 20cm/sec, it could transport sediments as heavy as _____ if its flow velocity increases to 1.4m/sec during a severe flood.

23) If a fast moving mountain stream can normally transport pieces of gravel with masses up to 50 grams when its flow velocity is 50cm/sec, it could transport sediments as heavy as _____ if its flow velocity increases to 1.2m/sec after a significant springtime snow melt.

Lab 12: Earth's Structure and Plate Tectonics

The Earth has several basic parts of varying composition and consistency, which you should know, and its lithosphere is also broken up into several plates that move and interact with each other. So, it is also important for you to know how these plates interact and the features these interactions produce. The Theory of Plate Tectonics encompasses the mechanisms and the results of the interactions between these plates, and you should also know the evidence used to support this theory.

Objectives:

1) Learn the basic structure of the Earth, and the composition and consistency of each part.

2) Learn the types of evidence supporting the Theories of Continental Drift and Plate Tectonics.

3) Learn the materials/plates involved with tectonic activity and how they interact.

4) Learn examples of tectonic boundaries and features created by them.

5) Learn how far tectonic plates can potentially move over geologic time.

6) Learn the types of tectonic boundaries and their basic features.

Part I

It is important that you know the basic structure of the Earth, and the composition and consistency of its basic parts. Note that the compositions of the basic parts are silicate rock, granitic rock or basaltic rock, or iron-nickel metal, while their consistency is either solid, semi-solid (plastic), or liquid.

Using the images of Earth's structure on page 65, complete the following sentences:

1) The area marked with an "A" is the Earth's _Inner core_ (part), which is made of _Solid iron and nickel metal_ (use the consistencies and compositions from above).

2) The area marked with a "B" is the Earth's _Outer core_, which is made of _liquid iron and nickel metal_

3) The area marked with a "C" is the Earth's _Mantle_, which is made of _Semi-solid silicate rock_

4) The area marked with a "D" is the Earth's _Crust_, which is made of _Solid silicate rock_.

5) The area marked with an "E" is _Oceanic crust_, which is made of _Basaltic Rock_.

6) The area marked with an "F" is _Continental crust_, which is made of _Granitic Rock_.

7) The collective region marked with an "E", "F", and "G" is the Earth's _Lithosphere_, which is made of _Solid silicate rock_.

8) The area marked with an "H" is the Earth's _asthenosphere_, which is made of _Semi-solid silicate rock_

Part II

When the concept that continents "drifted" across Earth's surface was initially proposed, a great deal of evidence was needed to support it. So, four different lines of evidence were developed to support the *Theory of Continental Drift*. Over time, several additional lines of evidence were explored, leading to the development of the *Theory of Plate Tectonics*.

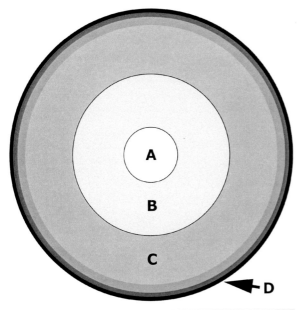

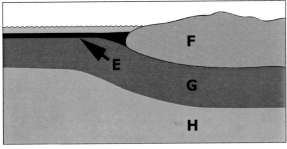

9) List the 4 types of evidence originally used to support the Theory of Continental Drift:

#1. Coastlines fit together

#2. Similarities in fossils found in different areas

#3. Similarities in rocks and mountains

#4. Paleoclimatic Evidence

10) List the additional types of evidence used to support the Theory of Plate Tectonics:

#1. Deep-Sea drilling & the dating of Seafloor rocks

#2. The dating of volcanoes created by hot spot activity

#3. Paleomagnetic Evidence

#4. Measurements of Plate motion using new technologies

Part III

Continents are essentially giant masses of granitic rock, while ocean floors are made of relatively thin slabs of basaltic rock. These two types of rock have different densities though, which plays a role in how plates interact with each other during tectonic activity.

Complete the following sentences:

11) Continental crust is composed primarily of ___granitic rock___, which has a density of about 2.7 g/cm³

12) Oceanic crust is composed primarily of ___Basaltic rock___, which has a density of about 3.0 g/cm³.

13) If oceanic crust converges with continental crust, the ___oceanic___ crust will be subducted under the ___continental___ crust.

14) If continental crust converges with continental crust, ___folded mountains___ will be formed.

15) If older, relatively cool oceanic crust converges with younger, relatively warm oceanic crust, the ___older___ and slightly more dense crust will typically be subducted under the ___younger___ and less dense crust.

Part IV

Learning real-world examples of plate interactions and the features they produce can help you better understand how they form or work, and you might visit some of them one day (if you haven't already).

Complete the following sentences:

16) A good example of mountains created by continental–continental convergence would be the ___Himalaya___ Mountains.

17) Indonesia is a volcanic island arc created by the subduction of ___oceanic___ crust under ___oceanic___ crust.

18) A good example of a feature created by a transform boundary on the edge of the North American Plate would be the ___San-Andreas fault___.

19) The Aleutian Islands of Alaska are a good example of a volcanic island arc created by a
    _Oceanic   convergent_____ boundary.

20) The Mid-Atlantic Ridge is a good example of an _Oceanic-Oceanic   divergent_____ boundary.

21) A good example of a rift zone created by a divergent boundary on a continent would be the
    _African rift zone_____.

22) The Andes Mountains of South America are a good example of a volcanic arc created by a
    _oceanic convergent boundary_____ boundary.

23) Another good example of a volcanic arc created by oceanic–continental convergence would be the
    _Cascade_____ Mountains of the American Northwest.

Part V

Earth's lithospheric plates move across its surface at variable rates. For example, the Juan de Fuca plate is moving eastward at a relatively slowly rate of about 1.25 inches per year, while the Pacific plate is moving northwest at a relatively rapid pace of about 4 to 6 inches per year, depending on where measured. While these movements may seem very slow on a human time scale, plates can still move vast distances on a geologic time scale. In fact, even moving at only a few inches per year, a plate could potentially make several laps around the Earth's surface over the billions of years that it has existed.

Answer the following questions: 5×1000000

24) If a plate is moving at a rate of 1.25 inches per year, how many miles can it move in 1 million years?
    $1.25 \times 1,000,000 = 1,250,000$ in $1250000 / 63,360 = 19.7$

25) How many miles could the same plate move in 100 million years?
    $19.7 \times 100 = 1970$

26) How many miles could the same plate move in 1,000 million years (1 billion years)?
    $19.7 \times 1000 = 19700$

27) If a plate is moving at a rate of 6 inches per year, how many miles can it move in 1 million years?
    $6 \times 1m = 6m$ $6m / 63,360 = 94.7$

28) How many miles could the same plate move in 100 million years?
    94.7×100 9470

29) How many miles could the same plate move in 1,000 million years (1 billion years)?
    94.7×1000 94700

30) Earth's circumference is approximately 25,000 miles. What is its circumference in inches?
    $25000 \times 63360 = 1,584,000,000$

31) In a hypothetical situation, how many years would it take a plate moving at a rate of 1.25 inches per year to "make a lap" all of the way around the Earth?
    $1,584,000,000 / 1.25 = 1,267,200,200$

32) In a hypothetical situation, how many years would it take a plate moving at a rate of 6 inches per year to "make a lap" all of the way around the Earth?

33) The Earth's tectonic plates developed over a period of a many hundreds of millions of years after the planet formed, and plate tectonic activity is thought to have begun approximately 3.5 billion years ago. In a hypothetical situation, if a plate formed this long ago and began moving in a straight line around the Earth at 6 inches per year since, how many laps would it have made around the Earth by now?

66

Part VI

Name: Joseph McCulliss

Make a simple sketch of each type of plate boundary in the spaces below. Label the following features on each diagram where applicable: continental crust, oceanic crust, rift, subduction zone, trench, magma, volcanic arc, volcanic island arc, and fold mountains.

Note: This page must be completed and turned in with the quiz covering this lab.

continental divergent boundary

Continetal Crust Rift Contnetal Crust

Magma

oceanic divergent boundary

Rift

oceanic crust

Magma

oceanic–continental convergent boundary

Trench   Volcanic arc

Contnetal Crust
or Magma

oceanic crust

Subduction Zone

oceanic–oceanic convergent boundary

Volcanic island arc   Trench

oceanicCrust

Magma   Subduction Zone

continental–continental convergent boundary

Continental   Crust

Subducted Oceanic Crust

transform boundary

movement of plates

Lab 13: Seismic Waves and Earthquakes

Earthquakes occur by the thousands each year, but most of them do not cause damage or loss of life. Still, in many locations around the world, they are a threat to humans, and when they do harm, their locations and magnitudes are often reported in the media. Thus, it is important for you to understand how earthquakes are located and how their magnitude is measured.

Objectives:

1) Learn the types of seismic waves and the differences between them.

2) Learn how to calculate the variance in shaking and energy required/released by earthquakes.

3) Learn how to determine the location of an earthquake's epicenter.

Part I

Earthquakes produce shock waves, which are properly called *seismic waves*, with some traveling through the Earth and others spreading out across the Earth's surface. Those that travel through the Earth are called *body waves*, and those that travel across the surface are called *surface waves*. Body waves also come in two forms, *primary waves* (P waves) and *secondary waves* (S waves), both of which are unique.

P waves are compressional waves that can travel though solids and liquids, while S waves are shear waves that can only travel through solids. P waves also travel through materials about 1.7 times faster than S waves, or about twice as fast. And, surface waves are the slowest of the three.

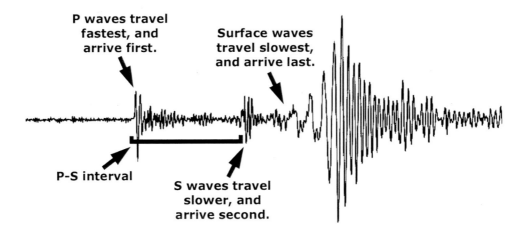

Complete the following sentences:

1) The two basic types of seismic waves are ___Surface___ and ___body___ waves.

2) The two types of seismic *body* waves are ___Primary___ and ___Secondary___ waves.

3) Primary waves are ___Compressional___ in nature.

4) Primary waves can travel through ___Solids___ and ___liquids___, and travel about ___twice___ times as fast as secondary waves.

5) Secondary waves are ___Shear___ in nature.

6) Secondary waves can travel only through ___Solids___ .

Part II

The strength of an earthquake is often reported by the media as its magnitude on the *Richter Scale*, but the U.S. Geologic Survey now uses an improved scale known as the *Moment-Magnitude Scale*. Both scales can be deceptive though, as an increase of 1 on either scale equates to a ten-fold increase in ground shake. For example, if one earthquake registers as a 4 and another earthquake registers as a 5, this means that the second earthquake shook the ground 10 times harder than the first. For all practical purposes, earthquakes registering up to about 6.5 on the Richter Scale will have the same ranking on the Moment–Magnitude Scale. However, for those beyond 6.5, the Moment-Magnitude numbers become somewhat larger, with up to nearly a whole number increase over Richter numbers for the most powerful earthquakes.

With this in mind it should make sense then that a magnitude 1 to 2 earthquake on either scale can't even be felt by humans, while a 4 to 4.9 can be felt by most people in the area, and a 5 to 5.9 produces damaging shocks. That's a big jump from being "felt by most" to "damaging shocks" when going up just one number from a 4 to a 5, but again, that's because a 5 shakes the ground 10 times harder than a 4. Understanding this should also shed some light on why earthquakes with magnitudes greater than 8 can be catastrophic, as they shake the ground at least 1,000 times harder than a 5, which can cause minor damage.

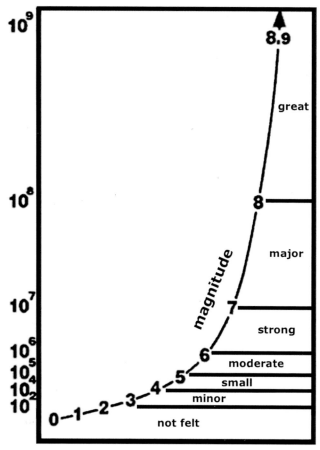

Here's an example of how this can be determined: A magnitude 6 earthquake will shake the ground 10 times harder than a 5. And, a magnitude 7 earthquake will shake the ground 10 times harder than a 6. And, a magnitude 8 earthquake will shake the ground 10 times harder than a 7. So, that's 10 x 10 x 10 = 1,000 (not 30 + 30 + 30). The shorter way to look at it is that an earthquake with a magnitude of 8 is 3 whole numbers higher than a 5, and 10^3 equals 1,000.

The amount of energy required/released during an earthquake also increases rapidly in relation to its magnitude. You'd think that it would take 10 times as much energy to make the ground shake 10 times harder, but it actually takes about 30 times as much energy. So, as in the case of ground shake above, each increase of one whole number equates to a roughly thirty-fold increase in energy required/released. Thus, a magnitude 5 earthquake would require/release about 30 times more energy than a 4, and an 8 would require/release about 27,000 times as much energy as a 5.

Again, here's an example of how this can be determined: A magnitude 6 earthquake will require/release 30 times as much energy as a 5. And, a magnitude 7 earthquake will require/release 30 times as much energy as a 6. And, a magnitude 8 earthquake will require/release 30 times as much energy as a 7. So, that's 30 x 30 x 30 = 27,000. Again, the shorter way to look at it is that an earthquake with a magnitude of 8 is 3 whole numbers higher than a 5, and 30^3 equals 27,000. $6-2=4 \quad 10^4$

Complete the following sentences:

7) A magnitude 6 earthquake will shake the ground about __10000__ times harder than a magnitude 2 earthquake. $7-3=4 \quad 10^4$

8) A magnitude 7 earthquake will shake the ground about __10000__ times harder than a magnitude 3 earthquake.

$8-3 = 5 \; 10^5 \qquad\qquad 6-2= 4$

9) A magnitude 8 earthquake will shake the ground about __100,000__ times harder than a magnitude 3 earthquake.

10) A magnitude 6 earthquake requires/releases about __810,000__ times more energy than a magnitude 2 earthquake. $6-2=4 \quad 30^4$

11) A magnitude 7 earthquake requires/releases about __810,000__ times more energy than a magnitude 3 earthquake.

12) A magnitude 8 earthquake requires/releases about __24,300,000__ times more energy than a magnitude 3 earthquake.

13) The strongest earthquake recorded, which occurred in 1960 in Chile, had a magnitude of 9.5 on the Moment-Magnitude Scale. The ground shake produced by this earthquake was __100000__ times stronger, and there was __24300000__ more energy required/released, than that of a magnitude 4.5 earthquake, which is typically non-destructive and may not even be felt by all people in the area.

Part III

Earthquakes can be detected through the use of an instrument called a *seismograph* that can record seismic activity on a *seismogram*, which is a paper or digital record of seismic waves and their intensity. The distance to an earthquake's epicenter can then be determined by measuring the amount of time that passes between the arrival of the first primary waves and the first secondary waves at a given location, which is called the *P-S interval*.

This is possible because geologists (more specifically, seismologists) have studied the behavior of these waves in great detail and developed a *Travel-Time Graph*, which can be used to find the distance to an earthquake's epicenter (see the graph on page 72). To use it, the P-S interval is found on the horizontal axis at the bottom of the graph, then a vertical line is drawn up to the travel-time (blue) line. The distance to the epicenter will be the number on the vertical axis straight across on the left side of the graph.

However, since this technique can only determine the distance to an earthquake's epicenter and not direction, data from at least three seismographic stations must be available to plot its location. Using these data, a seismologist draws a circle of the correct size (the radius of the circle is equal to the distance determined from the Travel-Time Graph) around the first seismographic station showing how far away the earthquake occurred. Then, another circle is drawn around a second seismographic station, and another is drawn around a third station. After this is done, all three circles should overlap each other, which would indicate the location of the earthquake's epicenter. Again, P-S intervals are needed from a minimum of three stations, which is why this technique is called *triangulation*.

Using the P-S intervals provided for three locations below and the Travel-Time Graph on page 72, determine and show the location of the earthquake's epicenter on the map on page 73.

Note: This exercise must be completed and turned in with the quiz covering this lab.

An earthquake occurs somewhere in the United States, and the body waves it produces are recorded at three seismic stations:

Station A is in Wyoming, and the P-S interval at this location is 3.3 minutes.

Station B is in Indiana, and the P-S interval at this location is 1.3 minutes.

Station C is in Texas, and the P-S interval at this location is 2.4 minutes.

Note that the map on page 73 has a scale of 1cm = 200km. This means, for example, that the circle drawn for an earthquake occurring 1,000km away should have a radius of 5cm on the map, as 1,000 / 200 = 5.

Also note that, if drawn properly, all three circles should overlap each other at one location, as shown in the example of triangulation on the right. This spot is where the epicenter of the earthquake should be drawn in with a dot and labeled as the epicenter.

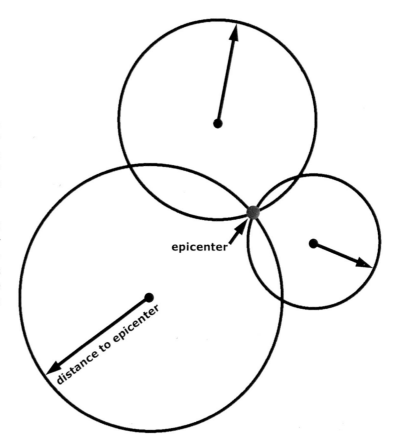

Travel-Time Graph

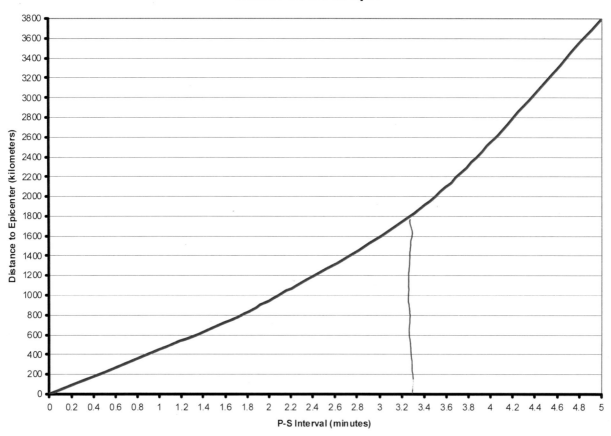

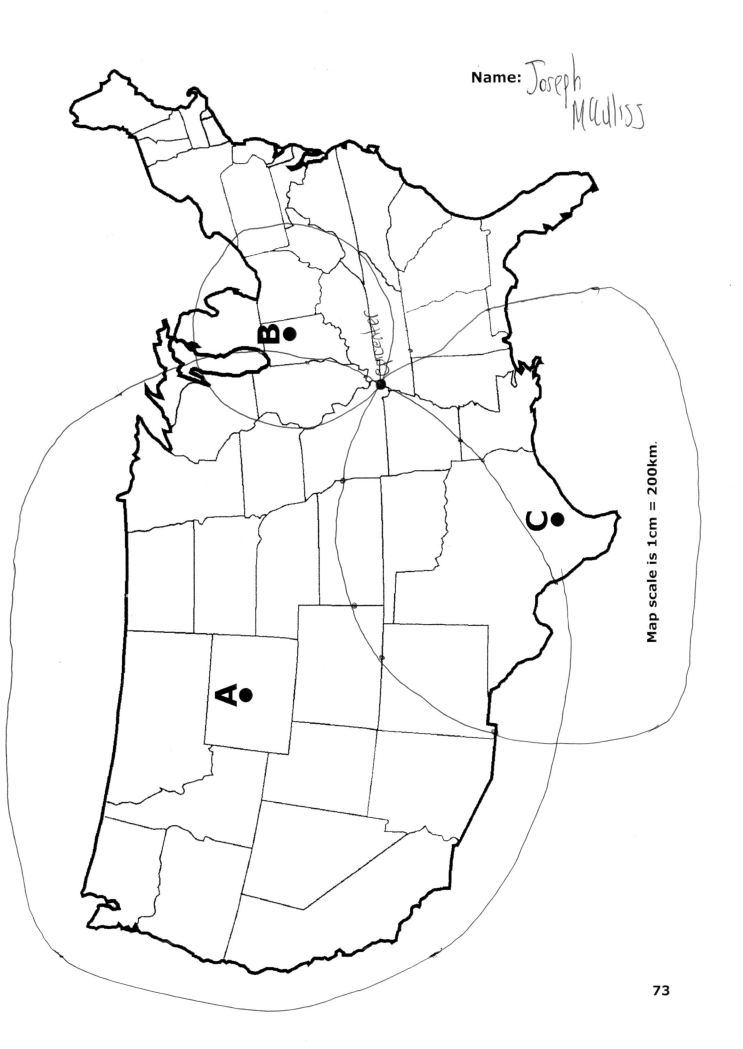

Name: Joseph McCuliss

B●

epicentre

C●

Map scale is 1cm = 200km.

A●

73

Lab 14: Volcanoes and Other Igneous Features

Volcanoes and volcanic eruptions can certainly be some of the most awe-inspiring natural structures and events on Earth, but all are not alike. There are three basic types of volcanoes, each of which is formed through the eruption of different types of lava and other materials, along with differing quantities of gas. So, it is important to understand what these materials are and how they erupt, and to know the different types of volcanoes they produce. Magma can also cool off and crystallize underground, forming intrusive igneous rocks, with a number of plutons being produced in the process. So, you will also need to learn what these features are and how to identify them.

Objectives:

1) Learn the materials erupted by volcanoes.

2) Learn the types of volcanoes and their basic characteristics.

3) Learn examples of each type of volcano.

4) Learn the basic intrusive igneous structures.

Part I

Volcanoes can produce *lava flows* and *pyroclastic materials*, and emit *gases*. There are two basic types of lava flows though, as well as four basic types of pyroclastics, and a variety of gases that may be erupted.

Complete the following sentences:

1) A highly viscous (thick) lava that resists flow would have a composition high in ___Silica___ and/or have a __low__ temperature.

2) __Basaltic__ lava tends to flow relatively well because it's typically relatively hot and low in silica.

3) __Rhyolitic__ lava doesn't flow well because it's typically relatively cool and high in silica.

4) __Ash__ and __Dust__ are the finest pyroclastic materials produced by volcanoes.

5) Medium-sized pyroclastic materials produced by volcanoes are called ___Cinders___.

6) The largest pyroclastic materials produced by volcanoes are called ___Blocks___.

7) Volcanic __Bombs__ are created when globs of lava are ejected from a volcano and then harden in the air, taking on a teardrop or football shape in the process.

8) The gas emitted in the greatest quantities by volcanoes is __Water Vapor__.

9) The second most abundant gas emitted by volcanoes is __Carbon Dioxide__

10) __Sulfur Dioxide__ is a harmful gas regularly emitted by volcanoes.

11) Relatively rough and blocky lava flows are called __aa__ flows.

12) Lava flows that are relatively smooth and rope-like are called __Pahoehoe__ flows.

Pyroclastic Materials

cinders

ash

blocks

bombs

Part II

Each type of volcano has some distinctive characteristics. Identify each type of volcano in the pictures on the next page, the primary type of material it's composed of (lava flows and/or pyroclastics), and it's size relative to the other types of volcanoes when fully developed.

Type: Shield   **Composition:**   **Relative size:** large

Type: Composite   **Composition:**   **Relative size:** Medvim

Type: Cinder Cone   **Composition:**   **Relative size:** small

Complete the following sentences:

13) A composite volcano can also be called a _____.

14) If large outpourings of pyroclastic materials pile up around a volcanic vent, a _____ volcano will form over time.

15) While they all start small, those that become the largest type of volcano are _____ volcanoes.

16) _____ volcanoes tend to have the greatest overall slope.

17) _____ volcanoes tend to have the lowest sloping sides.

18) Alternating eruptions of lava flows and pyroclastics will produce a _____ volcano over time.

19) After reaching their full size, the smallest type of volcano is a _____.

20) _____ volcanoes are built by the non-violent eruption of basaltic lava.

21) _____ volcanoes tend to have a lower slope near their bases with a steeper slope near their tops.

Part III

Learning a few real-world examples of the geological features that we cover is important, and it's good to know the names of a few of the world's most famous volcanoes. You might visit some of them one day, too (if you haven't already).

Complete the following sentences:

22) The Roman city of Pompeii was destroyed in 79 A.D. by Mt. _____, which is a stratovolcano.

23) _____ is a typical cinder cone, which is located in northeast Arizona.

24) The largest mountain on Earth is the Hawaiian shield volcano _____.

25) _____ is a composite volcano in Washington state, which exploded in 1980.

26) A common subject in Japanese artwork, _____ is a beautiful stratovolcano near Tokyo.

Part IV

When magma melts or pushes its way into surrounding rocks and then cools, producing intrusive igneous rock, a number of features can be formed. All of these intrusive features are called *plutons*, and there are four basic types. In the event that magma cuts across/through other rocks and then cools, we say the pluton created is *discordant* in nature, while those that form when magma squeezes between layers of rock are *concordant* in nature. Also, if the pluton is relatively flat in form (this does not mean horizontal), we say it is *tabular*, while those that are not flat are referred to as *massive*.

Any discordant and tabular pluton is called a *dike*, while any concordant and tabular pluton is a *sill*. And, any large, discordant, and massive pluton is called a *batholith*, while any concordant and massive pluton is called a *laccolith*.

In addition, when magma cools inside the pipe of a volcano when eruptive activity ceases, a column of intrusive igneous rock is formed. If the relatively soft material that makes up the rest of the volcano is weathered and eroded away over time, this column, which is composed of relatively durable rock, may remain and is called a *volcanic neck*. Thus, a volcanic neck is an erosional remnant of a volcanic pipe.

Identify each of the following on the picture below: magma, dike, sill, batholith, laccolith, and volcanic neck.

Feature 1:	Silt	Feature 4:	Dike
Feature 2:	Neck	Feature 5:	Magma
Feature 3:	lacolith	Feature 6:	Batholith

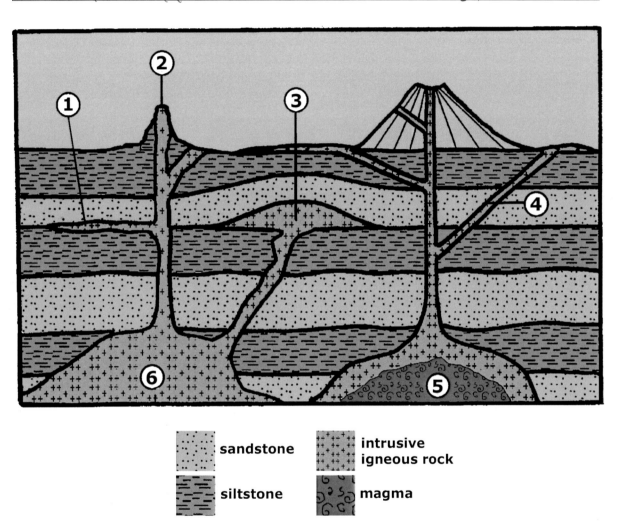

sandstone

siltstone

intrusive igneous rock

magma

Lab 15: Waves and the Tides

As waves interact with shorelines, weathering, erosion, and deposition can occur, all of which can modify the nature of coastal areas over time. In addition to waves, coastal areas are also subjected to cyclic, temporary changes in sea level called the tides. So, it is important to understand how these work.

Objectives:

1) Learn to identify the parts of a wave.

2) Learn how waves move through the open ocean and how they break on the shore.

3) Learn how wave refraction and creates beach drift and longshore currents.

4) Learn how the tides are formed and recognize spring and neap tidal configurations.

Part I

In the diagram below, the basic parts of a wave are shown. The tops of waves are called the *crests* and the low points between the crests are the *troughs*. The horizontal distance from crest to crest (or trough to trough) the *wavelength*, and the vertical distance from trough to crest is the *wave height*.

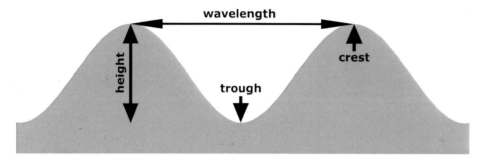

In relatively deep water, waves do not interact with the seafloor, and the water in and underneath a wave is moved in a circular manner as the wave passes. However, at a water depth equal to about *one half the wavelength*, which is called *wave base*, a wave will begin to "feel" the seafloor. As the bottom of a wave contacts the seafloor, creating drag, the movement of the wave slows and leads to a decrease in wavelength with a corresponding increase in wave height. Finally, the wave will break on the shore. Due to the fact that waves do not interact with the seafloor until the depth is less than wave base, waves can travel great distances in deep waters with little loss in their energy.

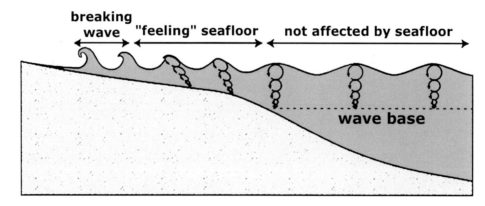

If a wave approaches the shoreline at an angle, it will begin to feel the seafloor as the first part of it reaches a depth equal to wave base. As this occurs, that part of the wave will slow down and the next part will catch up to it before slowing down, and so on. This has the effect of making the wave "bend" to the shoreline, in a process known as *wave refraction*.

As refracting waves break onto the shore, sand is moved in a zig-zag path down the beach. This process is known as *beach drift*. Just offshore, the process of refraction also sets in motion a movement of water parallel to the shore, known as the *longshore current*, which moves sediment, too. This transport of sediment and movement of water is responsible for creating a variety of common shoreline features.

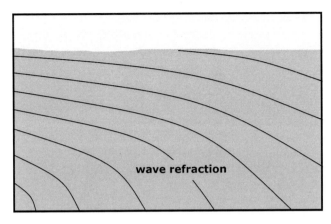

wave refraction

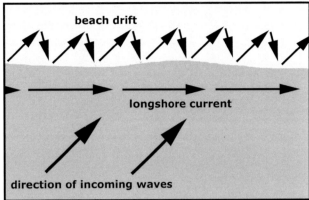

beach drift

longshore current

direction of incoming waves

Complete the following sentences:

1) The distance from the _trough_ of a wave to its _Crest_ is the wave's height.

2) The distance between the crests of two waves is their _Wavelength_.

3) As waves approach the shore they begin to "feel" the seafloor at about _1/2_ their wavelength.

4) If waves approaching a shoreline have a wavelength of approximately 30 feet, they would begin to feel the seafloor at a depth of about _15_ feet.

5) If waves approaching a shoreline have a wavelength of approximately 50 feet, the waves would begin to slow down and change form when the water became less than about _25_ feet deep.

6) The term that refers to the "bending" of waves to fit the shoreline is wave _refraction_.

7) The movement of sand and sediment along a shoreline is called _Beach drift_.

8) _Longshore Currents_ just off a beach also move sediment along coastlines.

Part II

The *tides* are the cyclic rise and fall of the ocean waters. Tides are caused by slight variations in gravitational attraction between the Earth and the Moon and the Sun in relationship to locations on the Earth's surface. However, despite the much greater mass of the Sun, the Moon is the primary factor controlling the nature of the tides, because it is much closer to the Earth.

The Moon produces two tidal bulges on the Earth through the effects of gravitational attraction. At the location on the Earth closest to the Moon, seawater is pulled toward the Moon because of the greater strength of gravitational attraction. And, simultaneously on the opposite side of the Earth, another tidal bulge is produced away from the Moon. However, this bulge forms because the pull of the Moon's gravity is at its weakest on the opposite side of the Earth.

As the Earth rotates, coastal locations move into and out of these bulges, causing most coasts to experience two high tides and two low tides daily. However, some locations will only experience one high tide and one low tide each day, while other locations may have irregular tidal patterns that are in between. The Moon also revolves around the Earth, making one orbit in a little more than 27 days. So, because the Moon moves around the Earth, the tides do not occur at the same time each day for a given location. Instead, the tides occur *about 50 minutes later each day*.

Again, while the Moon is the primary cause of the tides, the Sun's gravity contributes to the creation of tidal bulges, as well. When the Sun is aligned with the Earth and Moon, the combined effect of solar and lunar gravity enhances the tides. This higher than average tide, when the greatest tidal range is experienced, is called a *spring tide*. It is experienced twice monthly, during the new and full phases of the lunar cycle. Conversely, when the Sun and the Moon are perpendicular to each other with respect to the Earth, the Sun's gravity counteracts some of the Moon's influence, which results in a smaller tidal range. This lower than average tidal range is called a *neap tide*, and is also experienced twice monthly. However, it is experienced during the 1st and 3rd quarter phases of the lunar cycle.

The image below shows the phases of the Moon. On it, you can see that the Earth, the Moon, and the Sun are aligned during the new and full phases, which is responsible for spring tides. Likewise, you can see that the Moon and the Sun are perpendicular to each other with respect to the Earth during the 1st and 3rd quarter phases, which is responsible for neap tides.

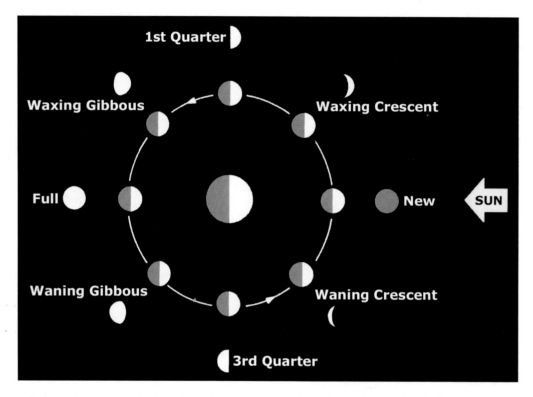

The image below shows a typical tidal cycle over a period of about a month. On it, you can see the influences of the changing alignment of the Moon and the Sun relative to the Earth as the Moon moves. Twice during the month they are aligned with respect to the Earth, creating two spring tides, while twice during the month they are perpendicular with respect to the Earth, creating two neap tides.

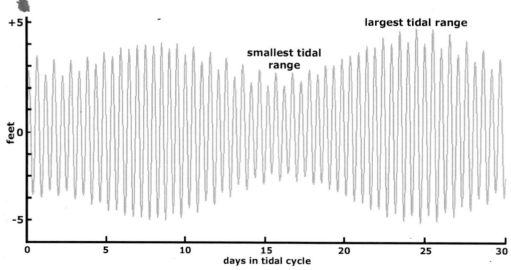

Complete the following sentences:

9) The two objects responsible for creating the tides are the __Moon__ and the __Sun__.

10) Most coastal locations will experience __2__ high tides and __2__ low tides in a 24 hour period.

11) If a high tide occurs at a typical location at 3pm on a Monday, the next high tide would occur at about __3:25 GM or tuesday__.

12) If a high tide occurs at a typical location at 3pm on a Monday afternoon, the high tide on Tuesday afternoon would occur at about __3:50 pm__.

13) When an area experiences the greatest difference between high and low tides (called the tidal range), a __spring__ tide is occurring.

14) When an area experiences the least difference between high and low tides, a __Neap__ tide is occurring.

15) When the Moon is in its __New__ or __full__ phase, the range of the tides will be at its greatest.

16) When the Moon is in its __1st__ or __3rd__ phase, the range of the tides will be at a minimum.

17) On the right, the upper diagram is illustrating the occurrence of a __spring__ tide.

18) On the right, the lower diagram is illustrating the occurrence of a __Neap__ tide.

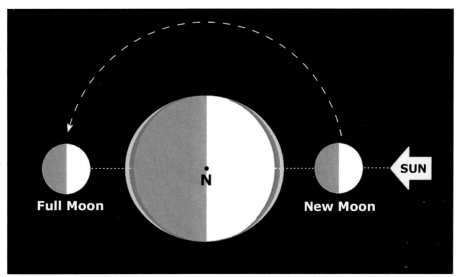

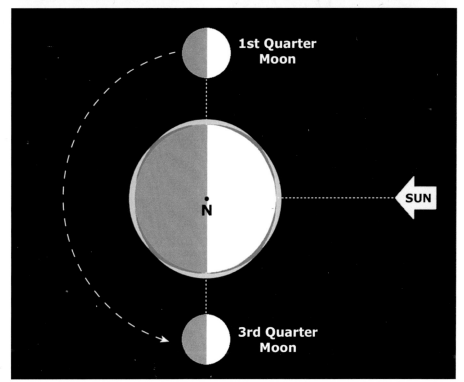

LAB 16: Radiometric Dating

Throughout history, people have had a desire to know the age of the Earth, and the folklore and religious beliefs of cultures all over the world have offered various answers to this age old question. In 1650, Archbishop James Ussher used the Judeo-Christian Bible along with the calendars and histories of several ancient cultures to deduce that the Earth was created about 4,000 B.C. However, in the 1780's, the new science of geology offered increasing evidence that the Earth was far, far older than a few thousand years. The discovery of natural radioactivity in the late 1800's and the development of an instrument called a mass spectrometer in the 1940's finally offered a reliable method to scientifically determine the age of rock specimens and, consequently, demonstrate the immense age of the earth.

Objectives:

1) Learn the parts of an atom and what an isotope is.

2) Learn about the concept of radioactive decay and half-lives.

3) Learn about the use of radiometric dating in determining the age of geologic specimens.

4) Learn about radiocarbon dating and how it differs from standard radiometric dating.

Part I

Matter exists primarily in the form of *atoms*, which are the smallest particles that still retain the properties of an *element*. There are 92 naturally occurring elements, and about two dozen manmade elements that have been created in nuclear reactors and experiments.

The identity of an atom is determined by the number of *protons* it possesses, which are positively charged particles found in an atom's *nucleus* (center). The number of protons equals the atom's *atomic number* seen on periodic tables. For example, hydrogen has only one proton, so its atomic number is 1. Helium, with 2 protons, has an atomic number of 2, and so on.

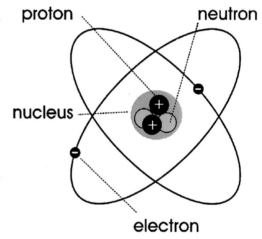

Most atoms also have neutral particles, called *neutrons*, in their nucleus, and atoms of a particular element may contain different numbers of them. This difference does not change an atom's atomic number though, since the atomic number is based only on the number of protons present.

Such atoms of the same element with differing numbers of neutrons are called *isotopes*. For example, carbon atoms (C) always have 6 protons, and thus always has the atomic number 6. However, they also have either 6, 7, or 8 neutrons. So, the three isotopes of carbon are C^{12}, C^{13}, and C^{14}.

Electrons, on the other hand, orbit the nucleus and have a negative charge.

Part II

Natural radioactivity involves the radioactive decay (breakdown) of the nucleus of an atom. When this happens, the original atom is transformed into either a different isotope of the same element, or into a different element altogether. In either case, the original isotope is called the *parent isotope*, and the product of the decay is called the *daughter product*. This process of radioactive decay and its timing is well understood by physicists, and the different rates of decay for each radioactive isotope is called its *half-life*. This decay process is not affected by heat, pressure, or other environmental conditions, either. So, the rates of decay of different parent isotopes can be used as a highly reliable geological clocks.

After the passage of one half-life, one half of the original material (parent) will decay into the product (daughter). In the next half-life, half of the material that remained from the first half-life decay will decay in the same manner. This results in the remaining parent material being divided by 2 with each half-life passage, with the daughter product correspondingly increasing. This progression is shown below and in the first table (notice how the numerators form the ratio):

Initially, there is no daughter product in the sample.

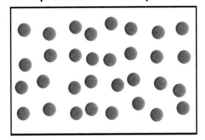

After one half-life, 1/2 of the parent atoms have decayed to the daughter product.

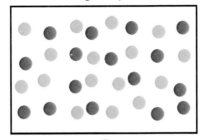

After two half-lives, 1/2 of the remaining parent atoms have decayed to the daughter product.

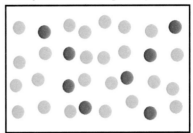

● atoms of the parent isotope   ● atoms of the daughter product

Half-lives Passed	Parent Remaining	Daughter Produced	P - D Ratio	P - D Percents
1	1/2	1/2	1:1	50/50
2	1/4	3/4	1:3	25/75
3	1/8	7/8	1:7	12.5/87.5
4	1/16	15/16	1:15	6.25/93.75

In actual practice, the parent-daughter ratio is determined using an instrument called a mass spectrometer. Then, with the ratio determined, the number of half-lives can be calculated and multiplied by the amount of time required for each half-life decay to occur for that particular isotope. However, our instruments have their limits, so it typically becomes difficult to accurately determine the parent-daughter ratio after several half-lives have passed because there will be so little parent remaining in a sample. Therefore, isotopes with relatively long half-lives are best suited to this process. Some of the most frequently used isotopes and their half-life values are shown on the table below:

Radioactive Parent	Stable Daughter	Half-life
Potassium^{40}	Argon^{40}	1.25 billion years
Rubidium^{87}	Strontium^{87}	48.8 billion years
Thorium^{232}	Lead^{208}	14 billion years
Uranium^{235}	Lead^{207}	704 million years
Uranium^{238}	Lead^{206}	4.47 billion years

Let's look at a simple example of how to calculate a specimen's age. If a rock sample has been determined to have a potassium^{40}/argon^{40} ratio of 1:7, then 3 half-lives must have passed (as can be seen on the table above). Since the half-life of potassium^{40} is 1.25 billion years (also from the above), the sample must be 3.75 billion years old.

3 half-lives x 1.25 billion years for each half-life = 3.75 billion years

Complete the following sentences:

1) If a specimen is determined to have 1/4 of its original amount of uranium^{235}, the ratio of uranium^{235} to lead^{207} would be _1:3_.

2) If a specimen is determined to have 1/16 of its original amount of uranium^{235}, the ratio of uranium^{235} to lead^{207} would be _1:15_.

3) If a specimen is determined to have a 12.5% of its original parent material present, its parent-daughter ratio would be _1:7_.

4) If a specimen is determined to have a 3.125% of its original parent material present, its parent-daughter ratio would be _1:31_.

5) If a specimen is determined to have a 1:3 parent-daughter ratio, _2_ half-lives must have passed since its formation.

6) If a specimen is determined to have a 1:31 parent-daughter ratio, _5_ half-lives must have passed since its formation.

7) After the passage of 3 half-lives, the remaining amount of parent material in a specimen would be only _12.5_% of the original.

8) After the passage of 4 half-lives, the parent-daughter ratio in a specimen would be _1:15_.

9) After the passage of 5 half-lives, the fraction of daughter product in a specimen would be _31/32_.

10) A specimen's uranium^{235}/lead^{207} ratio of _1:3_ indicates that 2 half-lives have passed since its formation. Therefore the specimen must be ___1.4 Byo___ years old.

11) A specimen's uranium^{235}/lead^{207} ratio of _1:31_ indicates that 5 half-lives have passed since its formation. Therefore the specimen must be ___3.5 Byo___ years old.

12) A specimen's potassium^{40}/argon^{40} ratio of _1:7_ indicates that 3 half-lives have passed since its formation. Therefore the specimen must be ___3.75 Byo___ years old.

13) A specimen's thorium^{232} and lead^{208} contents are analyzed, which indicate that 0.2 half-lives have passed since its formation. Therefore the specimen must be ___2.8 Byo___ years old.

Part III

The most common isotope of carbon in the environment is C^{12}, with C^{14} being present in much smaller quantities. C^{14} is an unstable isotope though, and is constantly decaying. However, it is also continually being formed at a known rate by solar radiation in the upper atmosphere, and scientists have measured the normal ratio between the two isotopes in the atmosphere.

Plants and animals maintain the same ratio in their tissues, because they are constantly taking in new C^{14} in their life processes. However, after death, no more C^{14} is taken in, and whatever amount is in their biomass at the time of death begins to decay. Therefore, the ratio shifts increasingly in favor of C^{12}. Unfortunately for geologists, C^{14} has a half-life of only *5,730 years*, though. So, this technique is limited to dating carbon-containing (organic) substances that are less than about 50,000 years old.

Complete the following sentence:

14) Analysis of a frozen mammoth carcass indicates that the C^{14}/C^{12} ratio of its tissue is 1:31. This means the mammoth died approximately ___28,650___ years ago.

Lab 17: Fossils and Stratigraphy

Living things are found virtually everywhere on this planet. Great and small, from plants, to animals, to microbes, they live in the oceans, on the land, in the atmosphere, and deep inside the Earth's crust. Still, over the long history of the Earth, it has been estimated that perhaps 99% of the species that have ever existed are now extinct. Most have left no trace of their existence at all, and thus relatively few are known to us by the remains or traces that they left behind. Regardless, we call these clues of past life fossils, and we will look at fossils in this lab.

This lab will also cover stratigraphy, which is the branch of geology that focuses on the study of rock layers (strata) in order to establish the framework of Earth's history. While we covered absolute dating in the previous lab, the basic concepts and principles of stratigraphy covered here are used to determine the relative ages of strata, and place geological formations and events in a chronological sequence.

Objectives:

1) Learn the definition of a fossil and the various ways that fossils may be formed and preserved.

2) Learn the basic principles of stratigraphy used in relative dating.

3) Learn to use the basic principles of stratigraphy to analyze stratigraphic diagrams.

Part I

Fossils are by definition, any remains or traces of past life, and the types of fossils and the manner in which they are preserved varies greatly. In order to be preserved, a deceased organism generally has to have some sort of hard body parts, such as a shell or bones, and be rapidly buried or otherwise protected from weathering and erosion. In addition, organic matter usually begins to decompose or fall victim to scavengers unless it is buried or preserved in an environment that prevents this from happening. So, as a rule, very few organisms ever become fossilized or leave other traces of their existence. Regardless, let's examine some of the ways things can be preserved:

Permineralization: If an organism is buried in sediments that contain mineral-rich water, the minerals in the water can soak into the organism's remains and begin to form microscopic crystals that fill in the voids and spaces within bones, teeth, etc., and even within the cells of some soft tissues. This often creates a fossil that contains some of the original hard parts of the organism reinforced by the precipitated minerals. Teeth and bones are good examples of this process. In teeth, the tooth enamel often remains essentially unaltered, but the soft pulp inside the tooth will largely be filled in by minerals. So too in bones, especially where marrow cavities become mineral filled and the spongy matrix of the bone itself becomes denser and harder from precipitated minerals. Note that *paleontologists*, scientists who study past life, call this process permineralization, but it is oftentimes called petrification.

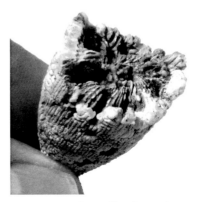

permineralized coral

permineralized shark's tooth

87

Replacement: If the permineralization process continues until the mineral matter not only fills the voids in the original remains, but also replaces the original hard substances as well, the specimen has been preserved by replacement. If the process proceeds slowly, the mineral replacement can occur on a microscopic level preserving even delicate structures, such as cell walls. This level of preservation can be observed in some fossilized wood, where every detail of the grain and fibers of the original wood is faithfully preserved. More rapid replacement may obliterate the internal structures though, as is often the case when wood or bone is agatized (when it is replaced by quartz) and lacks internal detail.

replaced (petrified) wood

replaced coral

Molds and casts: At times organisms are buried by a soft material that later hardens around them, leading to the formation of a *mold*. If the organism inside the mold then deteriorates and/or has its hard parts dissolved away by water, an empty void will be formed. If the mold is broken open it will reveal the external form of the original in a negative form. Sometimes molds may also be filled in over time by precipitated minerals, forming a *cast*. Many casts will display remarkable detail externally, but will lack any internal features. Shellfish, such as clams and snails are common examples of both mold and cast type fossils. Likewise, a rare example of this process occurring to humans is found at the city of Pompeii, Italy where victims were covered by volcanic ash that subsequently hardened and formed molds. After nearly two millennia, the bodies have deteriorated, leaving the empty molds, which are often filled with plaster by archeologists to create casts of the dead.

mold of a brachiopod shell

cast of a clam shell

Carbonization: Organic matter contains a great deal of carbon and under the right circumstances, usually requiring an oxygen-free environment, the carbon in the remains of an organism may be left behind when the other components of the organism's tissues are removed. The result can be a spectacular shiny black film that looks like a pen and ink drawing. This process seems to work best on smaller and thinner organisms such as insects, plant leaves, and small fish. It is also worth noting that the organic matter of buried organisms is typically converted into the coal and oil that we know as fossil fuels through such geologic processes.

carbonized fish   **carbonized fern leaf**

Amber Encapsulation: Some species of plants, notably coniferous trees, produce sticky resinous sap which can trap organisms and subsequently cover them, sealing them away from the elements. These resins are also antiseptic in nature and prevent the decomposition of the trapped organism. Over time the resin may undergo chemical changes itself, turning into a durable substance called *amber*. While they are rare, these fossils, which include insects, small reptiles and amphibians, and even some small mammals, are preserved in stunning detail.

bugs preserved in amber

Trace Fossils: Trace fossils are markings, impressions, or other types of fossils that are left behind by organisms and provide indirect evidence of life, rather than the preserved remains of the body parts of the organism itself. These include footprints, tracks, and burrows. Also included are *coprolites*, which are fossilized feces, and *gastroliths*, which are the stomach stones ingested by some reptiles, dinosaurs, and their descendants, the birds. These aided in digestion by serving as internal grinding stones used to help pulverize tough plant-based foods.

coprolite   **dinosaur footprint**   **gastrolith**

Unaltered Fossils: In some cases, remains of creatures may be preserved in an unaltered state by rapid burial in low-oxygen environments, by freezing, or by drying. So, shells, bones, and teeth may sometimes be found with little or no alteration, even after the passage of millions of years. Also, in the frozen tundra of the Northern Hemisphere, Ice Age animals, including mammoths and musk oxen have been discovered frozen in the ice. The tissues of these animals have undergone little alteration, even after spending tens of thousands of years in the frozen ground. Likewise, in the Austrian Alps, the body of a man was recovered from a glacier in 1991. First thought to be a hiker or skier who died an accidental death, the man's remains were found to be 5,300 years old. He was so well preserved that his tattoos remained visible on his skin and an autopsy was able to determine what he had for his last meal (deer meat, wheat bread, and fruit).

Preservation by desiccation (drying) is another way organisms can become fossils. In arid environments, especially in the presence of certain minerals, tissues can become too dry for any significant decomposition to occur. Sometimes referred to as "natural mummification", large animals and even humans have been preserved in this way.

unaltered oyster shell

piece of unaltered ammonite shell

Complete the following sentences:

1) Any remains or evidence of past life are considered to be __fossils__.

2) One of the most common substances that is preserved by replacement is __wood__, though it is often said to be "petrified" by non-scientists.

3) The name for fossilized sap or resin is __Amber__.

4) Fossilization by __permineralzat d__ often creates a fossil that contains some of the original hard parts of the organism reinforced by the precipitated minerals.

5) Molds may be filled by precipitated minerals at times, leading to the formation of a __cast__.

6) __Replacement__ occurs when mineral matter not only fills the voids in original remains, but also replaces the original hard substances, as well.

7) The voids left by humans' bodies in the hardened ash around Pompeii are called __molds__.

8) __Gastroliths__ are stones consumed by some animals to aid in digestion.

9) __TRACE FOSSILS__ include preserved footprints, tracks, and burrows produced by animals.

10) The fossilized waste of an animal is called a __coprolite__.

11) Scientists who study past life are called __Paleontologist__.

The instructor will provide you with some fossil specimens to examine. For each specimen, make observations and determine the type of fossilization, and write them in the table below:

Fossil Name	Appearance/Description	Type of Fossilization

Part II

Again, *stratigraphy* is the branch of geology that focuses on the study of *strata* (layers of rock) in order to establish a framework of the Earth's history. Listed below are the basic concepts and principles used in stratigraphy:

The Principle of Original Horizontality: Sediments are generally deposited in horizontal layers, and those that are not horizontal have gone through some type of deformation.

The Law of Superposition: In undeformed sedimentary strata, the oldest rocks will be on the bottom and youngest will be on top.

The Principle of Cross-cutting Relationships: Faults and intrusions are younger than the rocks that they are found in.

The Principle of Inclusions: When a body of rock contains fragments (inclusions) of an adjacent rock body, the body containing the inclusions must be younger.

The Law of Fossil Succession: The types of animals and plants found as fossils change through time. So, when the same kinds of fossils are found in different rocks, the rocks must be the same age.

Unconformities: In addition to the principles of stratigraphy outlined above, another important concept in stratigraphy is *conformity*. When sedimentary strata are deposited in a continuous manner, providing an uninterrupted record of geologic history, the layers are said to be conformable.

However, if a break in deposition occurs, and perhaps weathering and erosion actually remove some previously deposited material before a resumption of deposition, the result will be a *disconformity*. The layers of strata are still parallel when a disconformity is present, but they are separated by such a period of non-deposition/weathering-erosion.

Conversely, if sedimentary strata meet at a significant angle, the boundary between them is called an *angular unconformity*. Angular unconformities form when older strata are deformed in some manner, such as tilting/folding during crustal deformation, and are modified afterwards by weathering and erosion before deposition resumes.

Lastly, where sedimentary strata are in direct contact with igneous or metamorphic rock, but the two are separated by a period of non-deposition/weathering-erosion, the contact is called *nonconformity*.

Indicate the type of unconformity illustrated below:

12) Nonconformity   13) disconformity   14) Angular Conformity

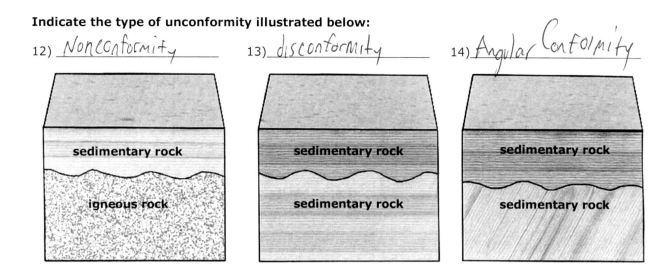

For the image below, use the principles of stratigraphy to determine the correct sequence. Fill in the blanks with the corresponding letters, from oldest to youngest.

oldest   D   B   A   E   C   F   youngest

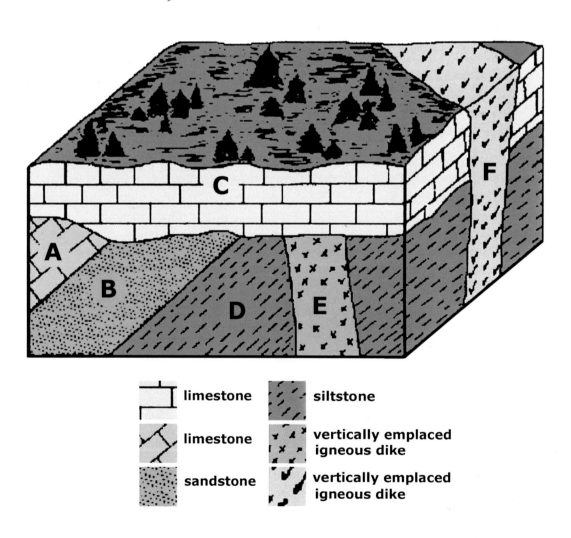

	limestone		siltstone
	limestone		vertically emplaced igneous dike
	sandstone		vertically emplaced igneous dike

Name: Joseph McCulliss

For the image below, use the principles of stratigraphy to determine the correct sequence. Fill in the blanks with the corresponding letters, from oldest to youngest.

Note: This exercise must be completed and turned in with the quiz covering this lab.

oldest E   D   F   H   J   I   C   B   A   G youngest

Also, identify each type of unconformity shown:

Unconformity #1: nonconformity

Unconformity #2: Angular Conformity

Unconformity #3: Disconformity

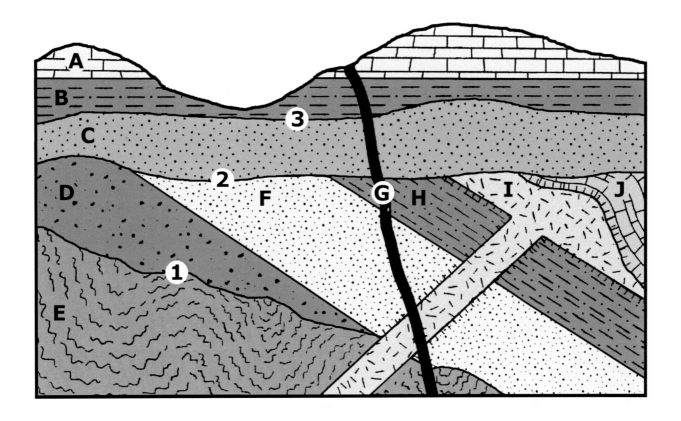

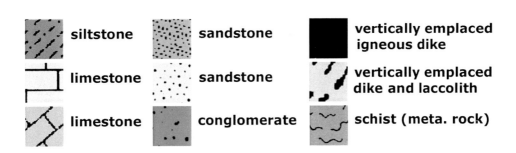

Earth Science Lab Exercises

Answers Section

Lab 1: Units of Measure

Part II

1) There are 1,080 inches in 90 feet.

      90' x 12 inches per foot = 1,080"

2) There are 6 inches in 0.5 feet.

      0.5' x 12 inches per foot = 6"

3) There are 126,720 inches in 2 miles.

      2mi x 63,360 inches per mile = 126,720"

4) There are 26,400 feet in 5 miles.

      5mi x 5,280 feet per mile = 26,400'

5) There are 3,168 feet in 0.6 miles.

      0.6mi x 5,280 feet per mile = 3,168'

6) A distance of 730 inches equals a distance of 60.8 feet.

      730" / 12 inches per foot = 60.83'

7) A distance of 262,000 inches equals a distance of 4.1 miles.

      262,000" / 63,360 inches per mile = 4.14mi

8) A distance of 14,000 feet equals a distance of 2.7 miles.

      14,000' / 5,280 feet per mile = 2.65mi

9) A distance of 3 miles equals a distance of 190,080 inches.

      3mi x 63,360 inches per mile = 190,080"

10) A distance of 7 miles equals a distance of 36,960 feet.

      7mi x 5,280 feet per mile = 36,960'

Part IV

11) There are 4,000 centimeters in 40 meters.

      40m x 100 centimeters per meter = 4,000cm

12) There are 30 centimeters in 0.3 meters.

      0.3m x 100 centimeters per meter = 30cm

13) There are 200,000 centimeters in 2 kilometers.

      2km x 100,000 centimeters per kilometer = 200,000cm

14) There are 5,000 meters in 5 kilometers.

      5km x 1,000 meters per kilometer = 5,000m

15) There are 400 meters in 0.4 kilometers.

 0.4km x 1,000 meters per kilometer = 400m

16) A distance of 850 centimeters equals a distance of 8.5 meters.

 850cm / 100 centimeters per meter = 8.5m

17) A distance of 122,000 centimeters equals a distance of 1.2 kilometers.

 122,000cm / 100,000 centimeters per kilometer = 1.22km

18) A distance of 14,000 meters equals a distance of 14 kilometers.

 14,000m / 1,000 meters per kilometer = 14km

19) A distance of 4 kilometers equals a distance of 400,000 centimeters.

 4km x 100,000 centimeters per kilometer = 400,000cm

Part V

20) A distance of 1,500 feet equals a distance of 450 meters.

 1,500' x 0.3 meters per foot = 450m

21) A distance of 6,500 meters equals a distance of 21,450 feet.

 6,500m x 3.3 feet per meters = 21,450'

22) There are 9,900 feet in 3 kilometers.

 3km x 1,000 meters per kilometer = 3,000m then 3,000m x 3.3 feet per meter = 9,900'

23) A distance of 8 miles equals a distance of 12.8 kilometers.

 8mi x 1.6 kilometers per mile = 12.8km

24) A distance of 53 kilometers equals a distance of 32.9 miles.

 53km x 0.62 miles per kilometer = 32.86mi

25) A temperature of 90° Fahrenheit is equal to a temperature of 32.5° Celsius.

 90°F – 32 = 58 then 58 x 0.56 = 32.48°

26) A temperature of 40° Fahrenheit is equal to a temperature of 4.5° Celsius.

 40°F – 32 = 8 then 8 x 0.56 = 4.48°

27) A temperature of 10° Celsius is equal to a temperature of 50° Celsius.

 10°C x 1.8 = 18 then 18 + 32 = 50°

28) A temperature of 45° Celsius is equal to a temperature of 113° Fahrenheit.

 45°C x 1.8 = 81 then 81 + 32 = 113°

29) If a sample of water has a volume of 300cm^3, then its mass would be 300g and its density would be 1g/cm^3.

   300g / 300cm^3 = 1g/cm^3

30) Seawater has salt dissolved in it, so a 1cm^3 sample of normal seawater would have a mass of 1.026g rather than 1g, and its density would thus be 1.026g/cm^3.

   1.026g / 1cm^3 = 1.026g/cm^3

31) If a 100cm^3 sample of Styrofoam has a mass of 10g, then its density would be only 0.1g/cm^3.

   10g / 100cm^3 = 0.1g/cm^3

32) If an oak log has a volume of 30,000cm^3 and a mass of 24kg (convert to grams), then its density would be 0.8g/cm^3.

   24,000g / 30,000cm^3 = 0.8g/cm^3

33) Granite has an average density of 2.7g/cm^3, so a 200cm^3 sample would have a mass of 540g.

   2.7g/cm^3 = Xg / 200cm^3, so 200cm^3 x 2.7g/cm^3 = 540g

34) If a sample of lead has a density of 11.3g/cm^3 and a mass of 500g, its volume would be 44.2cm^3.

   11.3g/cm^3 = 500g / Xg/cm^3, so 500g / 11.3g/cm^3 = 44.2cm^3

35) Gold is very soft when pure. So, most gold jewelry is only 1/2 (12 carat) to 2/3 (18ct) gold, which is mixed with other metals to make it stronger. Pure gold is exceptionally dense too, as a pure gold (24ct) necklace with a volume of 14cm^3 and a mass of 270g would have a density of 19.3g/cm^3!

   270g / 14cm^3 = 19.3g/cm^3

Lab 2: Earth-Sun Relations

Part I

A) summer solstice, on/about June 21

B) fall equinox, about September 21

C) winter solstice, on/about December 21

D) spring equinox, on/about March 21

1) 24 hours	4) 12 hours	7) 0 hours	10) 12 hours
2) 12 hours	5) 12 hours	8) 12 hours	11) 12 hours
3) 0 hours	6) 12 hours	9) 24 hours	12) 12 hours

13) If the first day of Northern Hemisphere summer is on/about June 21st, then the first day of winter, which is 6 months later, must be on/about December 21st.

14) If the first day of Northern Hemisphere spring is on/about March 21st, then the first day of fall, which is 6 months later, must be about September 21st.

15) If the North Pole has 24 hours of daylight in the summer, it must have 0 hours of daylight in the winter, and must also have 12 hours of daylight in both the spring and fall.

16) If the South Pole has a 24 hours of daylight on December 21st, then the North Pole must have a 0 hours of daylight on December 21st.

17) Since the Equator is right between the North Pole and the South Pole, it must have 12 hours of daylight every day of the year.

18) If December 21st is the first day of summer in the Southern Hemisphere, then it must be the first day of winter in the Northern Hemisphere.

Part II

19) If the Sun's altitude is 90º, it would appear straight up in the sky.

20) If the Sun's altitude is 0º, it would appear on the horizon.

21) If you wanted to see the Sun at an altitude of 90º at midday on/about June 21st, you'd have to be standing at 23.5ºN latitude.

22) If you wanted to see the Sun at an altitude of 90º at midday on/about December 21st, you'd have to be standing at 23.5ºS latitude.

23) If you wanted to see the Sun at an altitude of 90º at midday on/about March 21st, you'd have to be standing at 0º latitude.

24) If you wanted to see the Sun at an altitude of 90º at midday about September 21st, you'd have to be standing at 0º latitude.

25) The Tropic of Cancer is at 23.5ºN latitude, and the Tropic of Capricorn is at 23.5ºS latitude.

Part III

26) What would the Sun's maximum altitude be over Tampa on the winter solstice?

   Step 1: The Tropic of Capricorn at 23.5ºS

   Step 2: We're 28º above the Equator, and the Tropic of Capricorn is 23.5º below the equator, so add 28º and 23.5º to get 51.5º of separation.

   Step 3: 90º - 51.5º = 38.5º

   The Sun's maximum altitude over Tampa on the winter solstice would be 38.5º.

27) What would the Sun's maximum altitude be over Tampa on the spring equinox?

   Step 1: The Equator at 0º

   Step 2: We're 28º above the Equator, and the Equator is 0º latitude, so 28º minus 0º is 28º of separation.

   Step 3: 90º - 28º = 62º

   The Sun's maximum altitude over Tampa on the spring equinox would be 62º.

28) What would the Sun's maximum altitude be over Tampa on the fall equinox?

   Step 1: The Equator at 0º

   Step 2: We're 28º above the Equator, and the Equator is 0º latitude, so 28º minus 0º is 28º of separation.

   Step 3: 90º - 28º = 62º

   The Sun's maximum altitude over Tampa on the fall equinox would be 62º.

29) What would the Sun's maximum altitude be over Seattle on the summer solstice?

   Step 1: The Tropic of Cancer at 23.5ºN

   Step 2: Seattle is at 47ºN and the Tropic of Cancer is at 23.5ºN, so subtract 23.5º from 47º to get 23.5º of separation.

   Step 3: 90º - 23.5º = 66.5º

   The Sun's maximum altitude over Seattle on the summer solstice would be 66.5º.

30) What would the Sun's maximum altitude be over Seattle on the winter solstice?

   Step 1: The Tropic of Capricorn at 23.5ºS

   Step 2: Seattle is 47º above the Equator, and the Tropic of Capricorn is 23.5º below the equator, so add 47º and 23.5º to get 70.5º of separation.

   Step 3: 90º - 70.5º = 19.5º

   The Sun's maximum altitude over Seattle on the winter solstice would be 19.5º.

31) What would the Sun's maximum altitude be over Seattle on the spring equinox?

Step 1: The Equator at 0º

Step 2: Seattle is 47º above the Equator, and the Equator is 0º latitude, so 47º minus 0º is 47º of separation.

Step 3: 90º - 47º = 43º

The Sun's maximum altitude over Seattle on the spring equinox would be 43º.

32) What would the Sun's maximum altitude be over Seattle on the fall equinox?

Step 1: The Equator at 0º

Step 2: Seattle is 47º above the Equator, and the Equator is 0º latitude, so 47º minus 0º is 47º of separation.

Step 3: 90º - 47º = 43º

The Sun's maximum altitude over Seattle on the fall equinox would be 43º.

33) What would the Sun's maximum altitude be over Barrow on the summer solstice?

Step 1: The Tropic of Cancer at 23.5ºN

Step 2: Barrow is at 70ºN and the Tropic of Cancer is at 23.5ºN, so subtract 23.5º from 70º to get 46.5º of separation.

Step 3: 90º - 46.5º = 43.5º

The Sun's maximum altitude over Barrow on the summer solstice would be 43.5º.

34) What would the Sun's maximum altitude be over Barrow on the winter solstice?

Step 1: The Tropic of Capricorn at 23.5ºS

Step 2: Barrow is 70º above the Equator, and the Tropic of Capricorn is 23.5º below the equator, so add 70º and 23.5º to get 93.5º of separation.

Step 3: 90º - 93.5º = -3.5º

The Sun's maximum altitude over Barrow on the winter solstice would be -3.5º. *This means the Sun would not rise above the horizon, as it's maximum altitude is a negative number.*

35) What would the Sun's maximum altitude be over Barrow on the fall equinox?

Step 1: The Equator at 0º

Step 2: Barrow is 70º above the Equator, and the Equator is 0º latitude, so 70º minus 0º is 70º of separation.

Step 3: 90º - 70º = 20º

The Sun's maximum altitude over Barrow on the fall equinox would be 20º.

LAB 3: Humidity

Part I

1) A box holding 1 kilogram of air contains 4 grams of water vapor, so the specific humidity of the air in the box is 4g/kg.

   4g / 1kg = 4g/kg

2) A box holding 4 kilograms of air contains 12 grams of water vapor, so the specific humidity of the air in the box is 3g/kg.

   12g / 4kg = 3g/kg

3) A box holding 5 kilograms of air contains 25 grams of water vapor, so the specific humidity of the air in the box is 5g/kg.

   25g / 5kg = 5g/kg

4) A box holding 3kg of air with a specific humidity of 9g/kg must contain 27 grams of water vapor.

   9g of water vapor per each kg of air x 3kg or air = 27 grams of water vapor present

5) A box holding 6kg of air with a specific humidity of 2g/kg must contain 12 grams of water vapor.

   2g of water vapor per each kg of air x 6kg of air = 12 grams of water vapor present

Part II

6) If a parcel of air has a temperature of -10ºC, it would be able to hold 2 grams of water vapor per kilogram of air.

7) If a parcel of air has a temperature of 30ºC, it would be able to hold 28 grams of water vapor per kilogram of air.

8) If a parcel of air is heated, its water vapor capacity will go up.

9) If a parcel of air is cooled, its water vapor capacity will go down.

10) If a parcel of air is heated from 10ºC to 20ºC, its w.v. capacity will rise from 7g/kg to 14g/kg.

11) If a parcel of air is cooled from 40ºC to 0ºC, its w.v. capacity would fall from 47g/kg to 3.5g/kg.

Part III

12) If a parcel of air has a capacity of 10g/kg and is holding 5g/kg, the relative humidity would be 50%.

   5g/kg / 10g/kg = 0.5 and 0.5 x 100 = 50%

13) If a parcel of air has a capacity of 10g/kg and is holding 1g/kg, the relative humidity would be 10%.

   1g/kg / 10g/kg = 0.1 and 0.1 x 100 = 10%

14) If a parcel of air has a capacity of 15g/kg and is holding 13g/kg, the relative humidity would be 87%.

   13g/kg / 15g/kg = 0.867 and 0.867 x 100 = 86.7%

15) If a parcel of air has a temperature of 10°C and a specific humidity of 5g/kg, its capacity would be 7g/kg and the relative humidity would be 71%.

5g/kg / 7g/kg = 0.714 and 0.714 x 100 = 71.4%

16) If a parcel of air has a temperature of 30°C and a specific humidity of 5g/kg, its capacity would be 28g/kg and the relative humidity would be 18%.

5g/kg / 28g/kg = 0.179 and 0.179 x 100 = 17.9%

Part IV

17) When using a sling psychrometer, if the dry bulb reads 40°C and the wet bulb reads 30°C, the depression of the wet bulb would be 10°.

40° – 30° = 10°

18) When using a sling psychrometer, if the dry bulb reads 35°C and the wet bulb reads 30°C, the depression of the wet bulb would be 5°

35° – 30° = 5°

19) When using a sling psychrometer, if the dry bulb reads 30°C and the wet bulb reads 20°C, the relative humidity would be 39%.

The dry bulb is at 30° and the depression of the wet bulb is 10°. Use these with the psychrometric tables.

20) When using a sling psychrometer, if the dry bulb reads 36°C and the wet bulb reads 33°C, the relative humidity would be 81%.

The dry bulb is at 36° and the depression of the wet bulb is 3°. Use these with the psychrometric tables.

21) When using a sling psychrometer, if the dry bulb reads 20°C and the wet bulb reads 20°C, the relative humidity would be 100%.

The dry bulb is at 20°, but the depression of the wet bulb is 0°. If the depression equals zero, then there was no evaporation and no cooling of the wet bulb. This means the air must be saturated and the relative humidity would thus be 100%.

Part V

22) Does a dehumidifier change the specific humidity in a room? Why?

Yes, because it physically removes water vapor from the room.

23) Does a dehumidifier change the relative humidity in a room? Why?

Yes, because it physically removes water vapor from the room. While the water vapor capacity stays the same, this reduction of specific humidity would mean the air is further from saturation. So, the relative humidity would be lowered.

24) If you turn on a heater in your home or car, what effect does it have on the specific humidity? Why?

There would be no effect on specific humidity because water vapor isn't being added or removed.

25) If you turn on a heater in your home or car, what effect does it have on the relative humidity? Why?

> If the air is heated the specific humidity would stay the same, but the water vapor capacity would rise. If only the capacity rises then the relative humidity goes down, because the air would be further from saturation.

26) If you turn on an air conditioner in your home or car, what effect does it have on the relative humidity? Why?

> If the air is cooled the specific humidity should stay the same, and the water vapor capacity would fall. If only the capacity falls then the relative humidity goes up, because the air would be closer to saturation. However, since an air conditioner also strips water vapor from the air, the specific humidity does change in this case. In fact, the specific humidity is reduced so much that the relative humidity still goes down due to the removal of water vapor.

27) Why does water condense on a cold glass of water or soda, etc.?

> Because the cold glass, etc. reduces the capacity of the air in contact with its surface enough to cause condensation on it.

28) Why does water typically condense on the windows in a room if it gets cold outside at night?

> Because the air in contact with the windows in a room will cool much more than the air anywhere else in the room, and this reduces the capacity of the air in contact with the glass enough to cause condensation on them.

29) Why is it possible to "see your breath" in the winter, but not in the summer?

> Because your internal temperature is high and the water vapor capacity inside your lungs is very high, leading to a high relative humidity inside your lungs. When you exhale in the winter, this warm humid air is introduced to the cold air outside your body, which has a much lower water vapor capacity. If the capacity is low enough, water vapor will condense from the air you exhale, essentially forming a cloud as you breath out.

30) Why does a hair dryer dry your hair?

> Because it blows hot air with a very high water vapor capacity over your hair. This allows water to evaporate very easily.

31) Why does a "dry heat" like they have in Arizona feel so much better than the "hot and humid" conditions we have here?

> Because the air is hot and has a very high water vapor capacity, but is also relatively dry, allowing your sweat to evaporate very easily. Evaporation is a cooling process, so this evaporation of sweat cools your skin. The more evaporation there is, the more cooling there is. On the other hand, the air in Tampa tends to be much more humid, so it is more difficult for sweat to evaporate. If there is little or no evaporation of sweat, then there is little or no cooling. So, you feel much hotter and sweatier.

LAB 4: Air Masses, Fronts, and Weather Maps

Part I

1) A continental-polar air mass is abbreviated as cP, and the air within it is relatively dry and cold. C P

2) A continental-tropical air mass is abbreviated as cT, and the air within it is relatively dry and warm. C T

3) A maritime-polar air mass is abbreviated as mP, and the air within it is relatively humid and cold. M P

4) A maritime-tropical air mass is abbreviated as mT, and the air within it is relatively humid and warm. M T

Part II

1) Cold front:

2) Warm front:

3) Stationary front:

4) Occluded front:

Part III

9) What is the barometric pressure (in millibars) in the center of the low pressure system?

The barometric pressure is 997 millibars.

Also see Weather Map 1 on page 106

Part IV

See Weather Map 2 on page 106

Part V

14) What is the nature of the air masses in the area marked with a large A and the area marked with a large B on Weather Map 3, which are meeting where the cold front is shown?

A: relatively dry and cold

B: relatively humid and warm

Also see Weather Map 3 on page 107

Part VI

17) Using these maps to see the nature of the weather system, what would this type of large scale system be called?

The system is a mid-latitude cyclone.

Also see Weather Map 4 on page 107

Weather Map 1

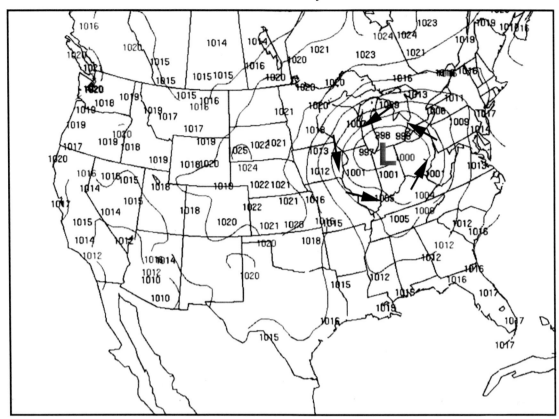

Weather Map 2

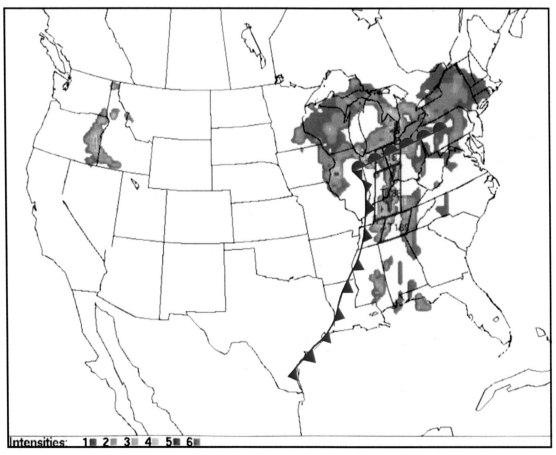

Intensities: 1 ■ 2 ■ 3 ■ 4 ■ 5 ■ 6 ■

Weather Map 3

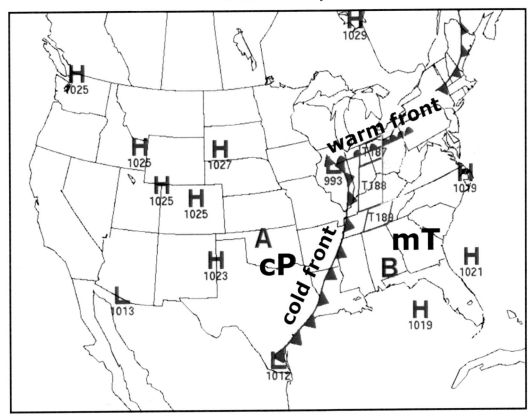

Weather Map 4

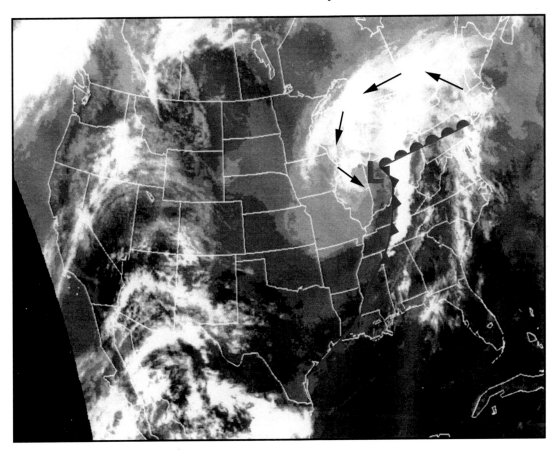

Lab 5: Severe Weather

Part I:

1) The "life" of a cumulonimbus storm cloud has three stages, which are the cumulus stage, mature stage, and dissipating stage. In the boxes below, make rough sketches of each of the three stages and use several arrows to show the updrafts and downdrafts that occur within the cloud during each stage.

Cumulus Stage   **Mature Stage**   **Dissipating Stage**

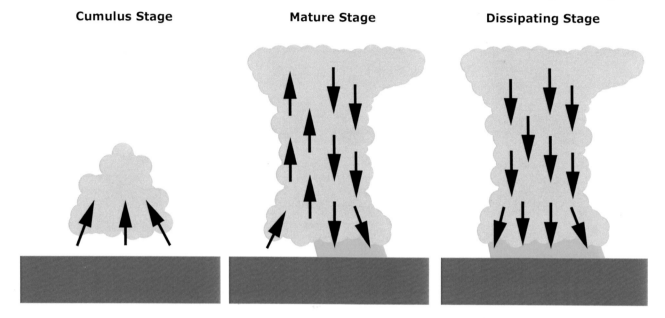

Part II:

2) If you are 6 miles from a thunderstorm and see a flash of lightning come from it, it would take about 30 seconds for the thunder to reach you.

   6 miles x 5 seconds per mile = 30 seconds

3) If you see a flash of lightning coming from a thunderstorm and about 10 seconds pass before you hear thunder, the thunderstorm must be about 2 miles away.

   10 seconds / 5 seconds per mile = 2 miles

4) If you see a flash of lightning coming from a thunderstorm and about 25 seconds pass before you hear thunder, the thunderstorm must be about 5 miles away.

   25 seconds / 5 seconds per mile = 5 miles

Part III:

5) On what scale are tornadoes ranked?

   Tornados are ranked on the Enhanced Fujita Scale.

6) What is this scale based upon?

   The scale is based on wind speed.

7) What time of the year do the most tornadoes occur in the United States?

   Most tornados occur in late spring through early summer.

8) If a thunderstorm produces a strong gust of wind moving at 50mph, it hits a house with a given amount of force. If a small EF-1 tornado formed and hit the same house with 100mph winds, it would hit the house with 4 times as much force.

100mph / 50mph = 2 (meaning the wind speed has doubled) and $2^2 = 4$

9) If the same tornado intensified to an EF-4 and hit another house with 200mph winds, it would hit the house with 16 times as much force as a 50mph wind!

200mph / 50mph = 4 and $4^2 = 16$

10) If the same tornado continued to intensify to an EF-5 and hit another house with 300mph winds, it would hit the house with 36 times as much force as a 50mph wind!!!

300mph / 50mph = 6 and $6^2 = 36$

Part IV:

11) If the maximum sustained wind speed produced by a tropical cyclonic weather system ranges from 0 to 38 miles per hour, what is the system called?

The system is called a tropical depression.

12) If the maximum sustained wind speed produced by a tropical cyclonic weather system ranges from 39 to 73 miles per hour, what is the system called?

The system is called a tropical storm.

13) If the maximum sustained wind speed produced by a tropical cyclonic weather system is 74 miles per hour or higher, what is the system called in the United States? What would it be called in Japan?

The system is called a hurricane in the U.S.

The system is called a typhoon in Japan.

14) On what scale are hurricanes ranked?

Hurricanes are ranked on the Saffir-Simpson Hurricane Wind Scale.

15) What is this scale based upon?

The scale is based on wind speed.

16) When are hurricanes most likely to form in the Atlantic/Caribbean/Gulf of Mexico region? In other words, when is our "hurricane season"?

Hurricane season runs from June 1st through November 30th.

17) Again, what are the three basic types of damage that can be caused by a hurricane?

Wind damage, inland flooding from heavy rainfall, and coastal flooding due to storm surge.

18) Historically, which of the above has caused the greatest damage and loss of life?

Coastal flooding due to storm surge has caused the greatest damage and loss of life.

19 through 21 are on the next page.

19) On the map below, mark the areas where tropical cyclones are likely to develop.

20) Also on the map below, mark the areas where the names hurricane, typhoon, and cyclone are used.

21) Lastly, on the map below, mark the most common tracks that tropical cyclones follow.

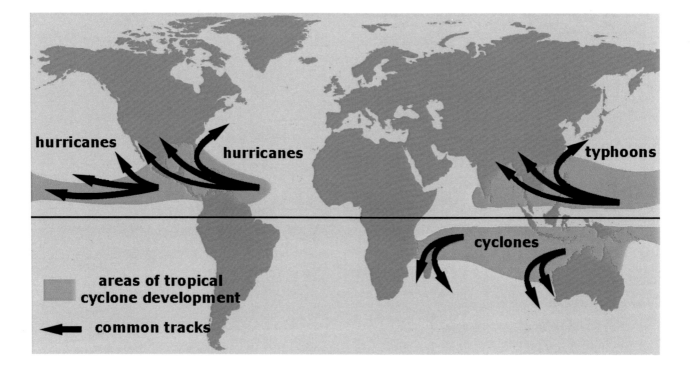

LAB 6: Topographic Maps Pt.1

Part III

1) The building at point A is 50 feet above sea level.

   You can find a 50 foot indicator if you follow the heavy contour line north.

2) The building at point B is 40 feet above sea level.

   You can find a 45 foot indicator on the next contour line up and to the northwest.

3) The building at point C is 60 feet above sea level.

   You can find a 50 foot indicator two contour lines down and to the northwest.

4) The building at point D is 47.5 +/- 2.5 feet above sea level.

   You can find a 50 foot indicator on the next contour line up and to the northwest. But, this building is between the 50 foot contour line and the 45 foot contour line. So, add 45' and 2.5' (½ of the contour interval) and then add +/- 2.5' (½ of the contour interval).

5) The school at point E is 42.5 +/- 2.5 feet above sea level.

   You can find a 50 foot indicator two contour lines down and to the southwest. But, the dot is between the 45 foot contour line and the 40 foot contour line. So, add 40' and 2.5' and then add +/- 2.5'.

6) The elevation of the intersection at point F is 47.5 +/- 2.5 feet above sea level.

   You can find a 50 foot indicator on the next contour line up and to the north. But, the intersection is between the 50 foot contour line and the 45 foot contour line. So, add 45' and 2.5' and then add +/- 2.5'.

7) The elevation of the surface of Wee Lake at point G is 32.5 +/- 2.5 feet above sea level.

   You can find a 50 foot indicator on the fourth contour line up and to the west. So, the surface of the lake must be lower than 35 feet, but also higher than 30 feet. So, add 30' and 2.5' and then add +/- 2.5'.

8) The elevation of the surface of the pond at point H is 32.5 +/- 2.5 feet above sea level.

   You can find a 50 foot indicator on the fourth contour line up and to the northeast. Also note that the tick marks on the contour lines around the pond indicate that the elevation is decreasing into a depression. Again, this means that the surface of the lake must be lower than 35 feet, but also higher than 30 feet. So, add 30' and 2.5' and then add +/- 2.5'.

9) The elevation of the surface of Chapman Lake at point I is 35 feet above sea level.

   In this case you can find the elevation of the surface of the lake printed on the lake itself. The blue "35" is the elevation in feet above sea level.

10) The elevation of the top of the hill at point J is 87.5 +/- 2.5 feet above sea level.

   You can find a 75 foot indicator on the third contour line down and to the northwest. Thus, the top of the hill must be higher than 85 feet, but also lower than 90 feet. So, add 85' and 2.5' and then add +/- 2.5'.

LAB 7: Topographic Maps Pt.2

Part II

1) The ground distance from the intersection at Point A to the intersection at Point B is 126,000 inches.

   The map distance from A to B is 5.25", and the map scale is 1:24000.
   So, it's 5.25" x 24,000 = 126,000".

2) The ground distance from the intersection at Point A to the intersection at Point B is 10,500 feet.

   It's 126,000" from A to B.
   So, it's 126,000" / 12 inches per foot = 10,500'.

3) The ground distance from the intersection at Point A to the intersection at Point B is 2 miles.

   It's 126,000" from A to B.
   So, it's 126,000" / 63,360 inches per mile = 1.99 mi.

4) The ground distance from the intersection at Point A to the intersection at Point C is 3.5 miles.

   The map distance from A to B is 5.25", and from B to C is 4".
   So, it's 9.25" x 24,000 = 222,000" from A to C, and 222,000" / 63360 inches per mile = 3.50 mi.

5) The ground distance from the intersection at Point A to the intersection at Point B is 319,200 centimeters.

   The map distance from A to B is 13.3cm, and the map scale is 1:24000.
   So, it's 13.3cm x 24,000 = 319,200cm.

6) The ground distance from the intersection at Point A to the intersection at Point B is 3,192 meters.

   It's 319,200cm from A to B.
   So, it's 319,200cm / 100 centimeters per meter = 3,192m.

7) The ground distance from the intersection at Point A to the intersection at Point B is 3.2 kilometers.

   It's 319,200cm from A to B.
   So, it's 319,200cm / 100,000cm per kilometer = 3.19km.

8) The ground distance from the intersection at Point A to the intersection at Point C is 5.6 kilometers.

   The map distance from A to B is 13.3cm, and from B to C is 10.1cm.
   So, it's 23.4cm x 24,000 = 561,600cm from A to C, and 561,600cm / 100,000 centimeters per kilometer = 5.62km.

9) The ground distance from the intersection at Point A to the intersection at Point B is 195,000 inches.

   Note: 1/8th of an inch is equal to 0.125 inches, as 1" / 8 = 0.125

   The map distance from A to B is 8.125", and the map scale is 1:24000.
   So, it's 8.125" x 24,000 = 195,000".

10) The ground distance from the intersection at Point A to the intersection at Point B is 3.1 miles.

   It's 195,000" from A to B.
   So, it's 195,000" / 63,360 inches per mile = 3.08 mi.

11) The ground distance from the intersection at Point A to the intersection at Point B is 494,400 centimeters.

> The map distance from A to B is 20.6cm, and the map scale is 1:24000.
> So, it's 20.6cm x 24,000 = 494,400cm.

12) The ground distance from the intersection at Point A to the intersection at Point B is 4.9 kilometers.

> It's 494,400cm from A to B.
> So, it's 494,400cm / 100,000cm per kilometer = 4.94km.

13) When using the curved road west of the interstate, the ground distance from the intersection at Point C to the intersection at Point D is 108,000 inches.

> The map distance from C to the left turn is 1.75", from the turn to D is 2.75", and the map scale is 1:24000.
> So, it's 4.5" x 24,000 = 108,000".

14) When using the curved road west of the interstate, the ground distance from the intersection at Point C to the intersection at Point D is 1.7 miles.

> It's 108,000" from C to D.
> So, it's 108,000" / 63,360 inches per mile = 1.70 mi.

15) When using the curved road west of the interstate, the ground distance from the intersection at Point C to the intersection at Point D is 276,000 centimeters.

> The map distance from C to the left turn is 4.5cm, from the turn to D is 7.0cm, and the map scale is 1:24000.
> So, it's 11.5cm x 24,000 = 276,000cm.

16) When using the curved road west of the interstate, the ground distance from the intersection at Point C to the intersection at Point D is 2.8 kilometers.

> It's 276,000cm from C to D.
> So, it's 276,000cm / 100,000cm per kilometer = 2.76km.

LAB 8: Topographic Maps Pt.3

Part I

1) If a map has 82º15′ at the top right corner and the same number at the bottom right corner, these would indicate the <u>longitude</u> of the right edge of the map.

2) If a map has 28º00′ at the top right corner and the same number at the top left corner, these would indicate the <u>latitude</u> of the top edge of the map.

3) If a location is exactly between 42ºW and 43ºW longitude, its specific longitude is 42º30′W.

4) If a location is between 65ºN and 66ºN, but is only 1/3 of the way up from 65ºN latitude, its specific latitude is 65º20′N .

5) If a location is exactly between 12ºN and 13ºN latitude and is also 3/4 of the way from 36ºE to 37ºE longitude, its specific coordinates would be 12º30′N and 36º45′E.

6) If a location is 2/3 of the way from 72ºS to 73ºS latitude and is also 1/4 of the way from 56ºW to 57ºW longitude, its specific coordinates would be 72º40′S and 56º15′W.

Part II

7) Each Township has dimensions of 6 miles by 6 miles.

8) The first Township north of the Baseline, and immediately west of the Principal Meridian would be T1N, R1W.

9) The third Township south of the Baseline, and immediately east of the Principal Meridian would be T3S, R1E.

10) There are 6 rows of Sections in a Township.

11) Each Section has dimensions of 1 mile by 1 mile.

12) The Section at the top-left of a Township is Section 6.

13) The Section at the bottom-right of a Township is Section 36.

14) The diagrams below show a black rectangle somewhere within Township 21 South, Range 14 East. The rectangle is also located in Section 23, in the NE 1/4 of the SE 1/4.

15) When written out properly, the location for the rectangle would be:

NE 1/4 of SE 1/4, Sec. 23, T21S, R14E

16) When written out properly, the location for the circle would be:

SE 1/4 of NW 1/4, Sec. 23, T21S, R14E

17) When written out properly, the location for the pentagon would be:

NW 1/4 of NE 1/4, Sec. 23, T21S, R14E

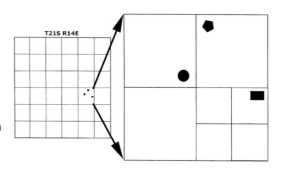

Lab 9: Minerals and Mineral Identification

Part II

1) Quartz is usually colorless to white in color, often forms six-sided crystals, and has no cleavage.

2) Calcite is usually colorless, white, or yellowish in color, often forms rhombohedral crystals, and has good non-cubic cleavage cleavage. The corners on a crystal have 75° angles.

3) Halite is usually colorless to white in color, often forms cubic crystals, and has good cubic cleavage cleavage. The corners on a crystal have 90° angles.

4) Pyrite is usually brass-yellow in color, and often forms cubic crystals. The corners on a crystal have 90° angles.

5) Galena is usually silver gray in color, and often forms cubic crystals. The corners on a crystal have 90° angles.

Part III

Specimen 1:   Halite

Specimen 2:   Galena

Specimen 3:   Quartz

Specimen 4:   Sphalerite

Specimen 5:   Graphite

Specimen 6:   Pyrite

Specimen 7:   Calcite

Specimen 8:   Magnetite

Lab 10: Rocks and Rock Identification

Part II

Specimen 1: granite

Specimen 2: scoria

Specimen 3: gabbro

Specimen 4: rhyolite

Specimen 5: diorite

Specimen 6: porphyritic basalt

Part IV

Specimen 7: breccia

Specimen 8: sandstone

Specimen 9: shale

Specimen 10: conglomerate

Specimen 11: siltstone

Specimen 12: coquina

Specimen 13: rock salt

Specimen 14: fossiliferous limestone

Specimen 15: chalk

Specimen 16: coal

Part VI

Specimen 17: gneiss

Specimen 18: phyllite

Specimen 19: marble

Specimen 20: schist

Specimen 21: slate

Specimen 22: quartzite

Part VII

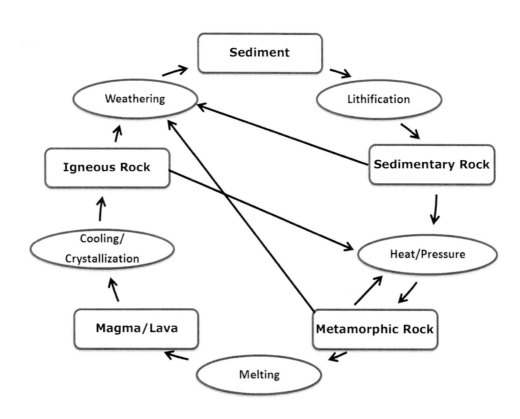

LAB 11: Streams

Part I

1) On the image below, label the cut bank and point bar areas of the stream channel, and the limits of the floodplain.

2) Also draw an arrow indicating which direction the stream channel is most likely to migrate over time.

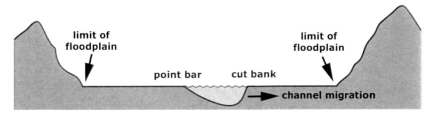

3) On the image below, draw heavy lines to show the limits of the floodplain.

4) Also circle at least three areas where oxbow lakes are likely to form in the future.

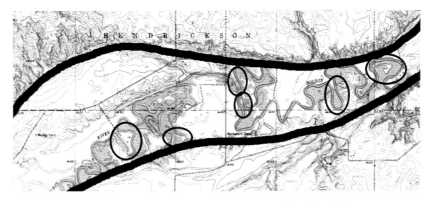

5) On the image below, label all of the cut banks, point bars, and oxbow lakes.

6) Also, draw several arrows indicating which direction each meander is most likely to migrate.

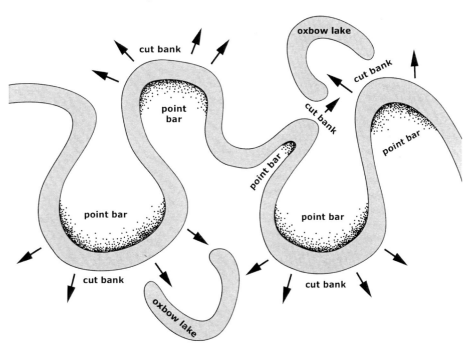

7) On the image below, draw lines/arrows showing where the highest water velocity is found in the stream channel (assuming that flow is from left to right).

8) Also on the image below, at the two marked points, draw a simple sketch showing the expected shape of the stream channel in cross-section.

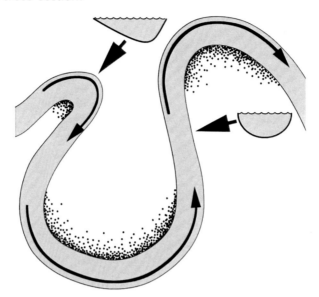

9) On the image below, label the headlands of the stream system, as well as its mouth.

10) Also on the image below, label the main meandering channel and the delta produced by the stream system.

11) What type of drainage pattern is shown in the headlands of this stream system?

     A dentritic drainage pattern is shown.

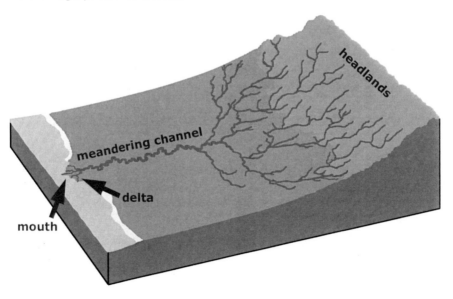

Part II

12) If a stream channel starts at 2,000 feet above sea level and ends at sea level, and covers a distance of 800 miles, the stream's gradient is 2.5 ft/mi.

    2,000ft – 0ft = 2,000ft   So: 2,000ft / 800mi = 2.5 ft/mi

118

13) The same stream's gradient would also be 0.05 percent.

800mi = 4,224,000ft   So: 2,000ft / 4,224,000ft = 0.0005 and 0.0005 x 100 = 0.05%

14) If a stream channel starts at 1,200 meters above sea level and ends at sea level, and covers a distance of 400 kilometers, the stream's gradient is 3 m/km.

1,200m – 0m = 1,200m   So: 1,200m / 400km = 3 m/km

15) The same stream's gradient would also be 0.3 percent.

400km = 400,000m   So: 1,200m / 400,000m = 0.003 and 0.003 x 100 = 0.3%

16) If a stream channel starts at 4,500 feet above sea level and ends in a lake at 600 feet above sea level, and covers a distance of 400 miles, the stream's gradient is 9.8 ft/mi.

4,500ft – 600ft = 3,900ft   So: 3,900ft / 400mi = 9.8 ft/mi

17) The same stream's gradient would also be 0.2 percent.

400mi = 2,112,000ft   So: 3,900ft / 2,112,000ft = 0.002 and 0.002 x 100 = 0.2%

18) If a stream channel starts at 2,200 meters above sea level and ends in a lake at 800 meters above sea level, and covers a distance of 700 kilometers, the stream's gradient is 2 m/km.

2,200m – 800m = 1,400m   So: 1,400m / 700km = 2 m/km

19) The same stream's gradient would also be 0.2 percent.

700km = 700,000m   So: 1,400m / 700,000m = 0.002 and 0.002 x 100 = 0.2%

Part III

20) If a stream can normally transport sand grains with masses up to 1 gram when its flow velocity is 20cm/sec in the winter, it could transport sediments as heavy as 4 grams if its flow velocity increases to 40cm/sec during a rainy summer.

40 / 20 = 2 and 2^2 = 4   So: 1 gram x 4 = 4 grams

21) If a stream can normally transport sand grains with masses up to 2 grams when its flow velocity is 20cm/sec, it could transport sediments as heavy as 32 grams if its flow velocity increases to 80cm/sec during a mild flood.

80 / 20 = 4 and 4^2 = 16   So: 2 grams x 16 = 32 grams

22) If a stream can normally transport sand grains with masses up to 2 grams when its flow velocity is 20cm/sec, it could transport sediments as heavy as 98 grams if its flow velocity increases to 1.4m/sec during a severe flood.

140 / 20 = 7 and 7^2 = 49   So: 2 grams x 49 = 98 grams

23) If a fast moving mountain stream can normally transport pieces of gravel with masses up to 50 grams when its flow velocity is 50cm/sec, it could transport sediments as heavy as 288 grams if its flow velocity increases to 1.2m/sec after a significant springtime snow melt.

120 / 50 = 2.4 and 2.4^2 = 5.76   So: 50 grams x 5.76 = 288 grams

Lab 12: Earth's Structure and Plate Tectonics

Part I

1) The area marked with an "A" is the Earth's inner core, which is made of solid iron-nickel metal.

2) The area marked with a "B" is the Earth's outer core, which is made of liquid iron-nickel metal.

3) The area marked with a "C" is the Earth's mantle, which is made of semi-solid silicate rock.

4) The area marked with a "D" is the Earth's crust, which is made of solid silicate rock.

5) The area marked with an "E" is oceanic crust, which is made of solid basaltic rock.

6) The area marked with an "F" is continental crust, which is made of solid granitic rock.

7) The collective region marked with an "E", "F", and "G" is the Earth's lithosphere, which is made of solid silicate rock.

8) The area marked with an "H" is the Earth's asthenosphere, which is made of semi-solid silicate rock.

Part II

9) List these 4 types of evidence originally used to support the Theory of Continental Drift:

   #1 The way some continents' coastlines fit together
   #2 Similarities in fossils found in different areas
   #3 Similarities in rocks and mountains found in different areas
   #4 Paleoclimatic evidence

10) List the additional types of evidence used to support the Theory of Plate Tectonics:

   #1 Deep-sea drilling and the dating of seafloor rocks
   #2 The dating of volcanoes created by hot spot activity
   #3 Paleomagnetic evidence
   #4 Measurements of plate motion using new technologies

Part III

11) Continental crust is composed primarily of granitic rock, which has a density of about $2.7g/cm^3$.

12) Oceanic crust is composed primarily of basaltic rock, which has a density of about $3.0g/cm^3$.

13) If oceanic crust converges with continental crust, the oceanic crust will be subducted under the continental crust.

14) If continental crust converges with continental crust, folded mountains will be formed.

15) If older, relatively cool oceanic crust converges with younger, relatively warm oceanic crust, the older and slightly more dense crust will typically be subducted under the younger and less dense crust.

Part IV

16) A good example of mountains created by continental–continental convergence would be the Himalaya Mountains.

17) Indonesia is a volcanic island arc created by the subduction of oceanic crust under oceanic crust.

18) A good example of a feature created by a transform boundary on the edge of the North American Plate would be the San Andreas Fault.

19) The Aleutian Islands of Alaska are a good example of a volcanic island arc created by a oceanic-oceanic convergent boundary.

20) The Mid-Atlantic Ridge is a good example of an oceanic-oceanic divergent boundary.

21) A good example of a rift zone created by a divergent boundary on a continent would be the African Rift Zone.

22) The Andes Mountains of South America are a good example of a volcanic arc created by a oceanic-continental convergent boundary.

23) Another good example of a volcanic arc created by oceanic–continental convergence would be the Cascade Mountains of the American Northwest.

Part V

24) If a plate is moving at a rate of 1.25 inches per year, how many miles can it move in 1 million years?

　　1.25 inches per year x 1,000,000 years = 1,250,000 inches

　　1,250,000 inches / 63,360 inches per mile = 19.7 miles

25) How many miles could the same plate move in 100 million years?

　　19.7 miles x 100 = 1,970 miles

26) How many miles could the same plate move in 1,000 million years (1 billion years)?

　　19.7 miles x 1,000 = 19,700 miles

27) If a plate is moving at a rate of 6 inches per year, how many miles can it move in 1 million years?

　　6 inches per year x 1,000,000 years = 6,000,000 inches

　　6,000,000 inches / 63,360 inches per mile = 94.7 miles

28) How many miles could the same plate move in 100 million years?

　　94.7 miles x 100 = 9,470 miles

29) How many miles could the same plate move in 1,000 million years (1 billion years)?

　　94.7 miles x 1,000 = 94,700 miles

30) Earth's circumference is approximately 25,000 miles. What is its circumference in inches?

　　25,000 miles x 63,360 inches per mile = 1,584,000,000 inches

31) In a hypothetical situation, how many years would it take a plate moving at a rate of 1.25 inches per year to "make a lap" all of the way around the Earth?

　　1,584,000,000 inches / 1.25 inches per year = 1,267,200,000 years

32) In a hypothetical situation, how many years would it take a plate moving at a rate of 6 inches per year to "make a lap" all of the way around the Earth?

　　1,584,000,000 inches / 6 inches per year = 264,000,000 years

Number 33 is on the next page.

33) The Earth's tectonic plates developed over a period of a many hundreds of millions of years after the planet formed, and plate tectonic activity is thought to have begun approximately 3.5 billion years ago. In a hypothetical situation, if a plate formed this long ago and began moving in a straight line around the Earth at 6 inches per year since then, how many laps would it have made around the Earth by now?

3,500,000,000 years / 264,000,000 years to make one lap (from #31) = 13.3 laps!

Part VI

Make a simple sketch of each type of plate boundary in the spaces below. Label the following features on each diagram where applicable: continental crust, oceanic crust, rift, subduction zone, trench, magma, volcanic arc, volcanic island arc, and folded mountains.

continental divergent boundary

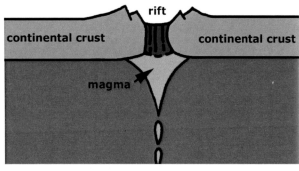

oceanic divergent boundary

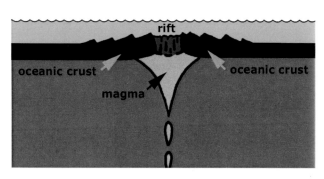

oceanic–continental convergent boundary

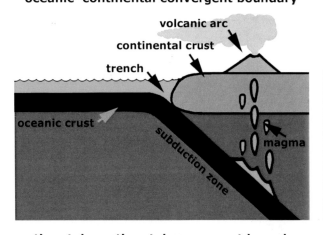

oceanic–oceanic convergent boundary

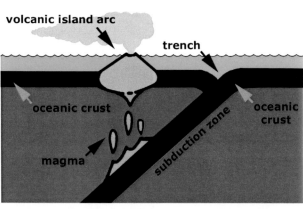

continental–continental convergent boundary

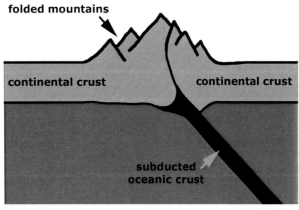

transform boundary

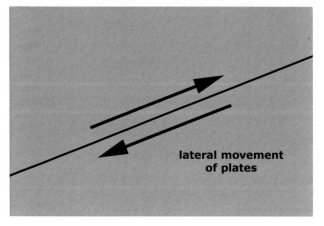

Lab 13: Seismic Waves and Earthquakes

Part I

1) The two basic types of seismic waves are surface and body waves.

2) The two types of seismic *body* waves are primary and secondary waves.

3) Primary waves are compressional in nature.

4) Primary waves can travel through solids and liquids, and travel about twice as fast as secondary waves.

5) Secondary waves are shear in nature.

6) Secondary waves can travel only through solids.

Part II

7) A magnitude 6 earthquake will shake the ground about 10,000 times harder than a magnitude 2 earthquake.

A magnitude 6 earthquake is 4 numbers higher than a 2, so it's 10^4 = 10,000.

8) A magnitude 7 earthquake will shake the ground about 10,000 times harder than a magnitude 3 earthquake.

A magnitude 7 earthquake is 4 numbers higher than a 3, so it's 10^4 = 10,000.

9) A magnitude 8 earthquake will shake the ground about 100,000 times harder than a magnitude 3 earthquake.

A magnitude 8 earthquake is 5 numbers higher than a 3, so it's 10^5 = 100,000.

10) A magnitude 6 earthquake requires/releases about 810,000 times more energy than a magnitude 2 earthquake.

A magnitude 6 earthquake is 4 numbers higher than a 2, so it's 30^4 = 810,000.

11) A magnitude 7 earthquake requires/releases about 810,000 times more energy than a magnitude 3 earthquake.

A magnitude 7 earthquake is 4 numbers higher than a 3, so it's 30^4 = 810,000.

12) A magnitude 8 earthquake requires/releases about 24,300,000 times more energy than a magnitude 3 earthquake.

A magnitude 8 earthquake is 5 numbers higher than a 3, so it's 30^5 = 24,300,000.

13) The strongest earthquake recorded, which occurred in 1960 in Chile, had a magnitude of 9.5 on the Moment Magnitude Scale. The ground shake produced by this earthquake was 100,000 times stronger, and there was 24,300,000 more energy required/released, than that of a magnitude 4.5 earthquake, which is typically non-destructive and may not even be felt by all people in the area.

A magnitude 9.5 earthquake is 5 numbers higher than a 4.5, so it's 10^5 = 100,000

A magnitude 9.5 earthquake is 5 numbers higher than a 4.5, so it's 30^5 = 24,300,000

Part III

An earthquake occurs somewhere in the United States, and the body waves it produces are recorded at three seismic stations:

Station A is in Wyoming, and the P-S interval at this location is 3.3 minutes.

Station B is in Indiana, and the P-S interval at this location is 1.3 minutes.

Station C is in Texas, and the P-S interval at this location is 2.4 minutes.

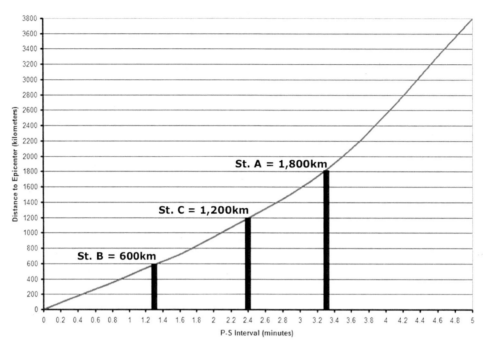

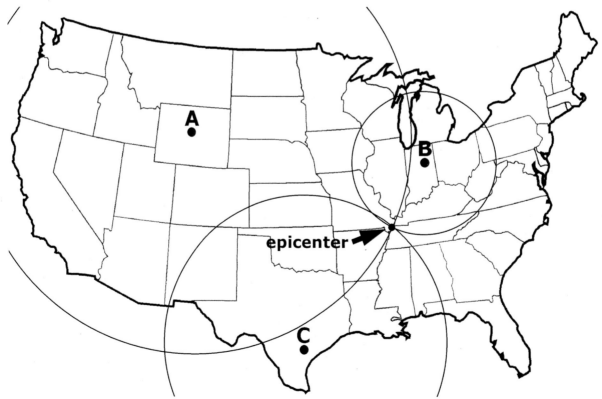

Lab 14: Volcanoes and Other Igneous Features

Part I

1) A highly viscous (thick) lava that resists flow would have a composition high in silica and/or have a low temperature.

2) Basaltic lava tends to flow relatively well because it's typically relatively hot and low in silica.

3) Rhyolitic lava doesn't flow well because it's typically relatively cool and high in silica.

4) Ash and dust are the finest pyroclastic materials produced by volcanoes.

5) Medium-sized pyroclastic materials produced by volcanoes are called cinders.

6) The largest pyroclastic materials produced by volcanoes are called blocks.

7) Volcanic bombs are created when globs of lava are ejected from a volcano and then harden in the air, taking on a teardrop or football shape in the process.

8) The gas emitted in the greatest quantities by volcanoes is water vapor.

9) The second most abundant gas emitted by volcanoes is carbon dioxide.

10) Sulfur dioxide is a harmful gas regularly emitted by volcanoes.

11) Relatively rough and blocky lava flows are called aa flows.

12) Lava flows that are relatively smooth and rope-like are called pahoehoe flows.

Part II

Type: shield volcano　　**Composition:** primarly lava flows　　**Relative size:** large

Type: composite volcano　　**Composition:** lava flows and pyroclastics　　**Relative size:** medium

Type: cinder cone　　**Composition:** primarily pyroclastics　　**Relative size:** small

13) A composite volcano can also be called a stratovolcano.

14) If large outpourings of pyroclastic materials pile up around a volcanic vent, a cinder cone volcano will form over time.

15) While they all start small, those that become the largest type of volcano are shield volcanoes.

16) Cinder cone volcanoes tend to have the greatest overall slope.

17) Shield volcanoes tend to have the lowest sloping sides.

18) Alternating eruptions of lava flows and pyroclastics will produce a composite volcano over time.

19) After reaching their full size, the smallest type of volcano is a cinder cone.

20) Shield volcanoes are built by the non-violent eruption of basaltic lava.

21) Composite volcanoes tend to have a lower slope near their bases with a steeper slope near their top.

Part III

22) The Roman city of Pompeii was destroyed in 79 A.D. by Mount Vesuvius, which is a stratovolcano.

23) Sunset Crater is a typical cinder cone, which is located in northeast Arizona.

24) The largest mountain on Earth is the Hawaiian shield volcano Mauna Loa.

25) Mt. Saint Helens is a composite volcano in Washington state, which exploded in 1980.

26) A common subject in Japanese artwork, Mount Fuji is a beautiful stratovolcano near Tokyo.

Part IV

Feature 1: sill (tabular and concordant)

Feature 2: volcanic neck

Feature 3: laccolith (massive and concordant)

Feature 4: dike (tabular and discordant)

Feature 5: magma

Feature 6: batholith (massive and discordant)

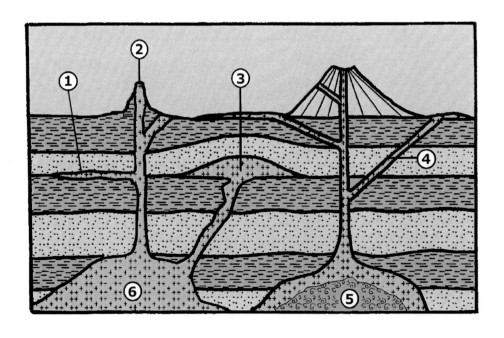

Lab 15: Waves and the Tides

Part I

1) The distance from the trough of a wave to its crest is the wave's height.

2) The distance between the crests of two waves is their wavelength.

3) As waves approach the shore they begin to "feel" the seafloor at about 1/2 their wavelength.

4) If waves approaching a shoreline have a wavelength of approximately 30 feet, they would begin to feel the seafloor at a depth of about 15 feet.

5) If waves approaching a shoreline have a wavelength of approximately 50 feet, the waves would begin to slow down and change form when the water became less than about 25 feet deep.

6) The term that refers to the "bending" of waves to fit the shoreline is wave refraction.

7) The movement of sand and sediment along a shoreline is called beach drift.

8) Longshore currents just off a beach also move sediment along coastlines.

Part II

9) The two objects responsible for creating the tides are the Moon and the Sun.

10) Most coastal locations will experience 2 high tides and 2 low tides in a 24 hour period.

11) If a high tide occurs at a typical location at 3pm on a Monday, the next high tide would occur at about 3:25am on Tuesday.

12) If a high tide occurs at a typical location at 3pm on a Monday afternoon, the high tide on Tuesday afternoon would occur at about 3:50pm.

13) When an area experiences the greatest difference between high and low tides (called the tidal range), a spring tide is occurring.

14) When an area experiences the least difference between high and low tides, a neap tide is occurring.

15) When the Moon is in its New or Full phase, the range of the tides will be at its greatest.

16) When the Moon is in its 1st Quarter or 3rd Quarter phase, the range of the tides will be at a minimum.

17) On the right, the upper diagram is illustrating the occurrence of a spring tide.

18) On the right, the lower diagram is illustrating the occurrence of a neap tide.

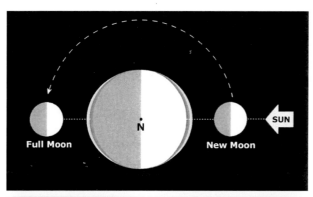

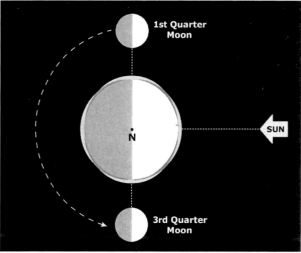

LAB 16: Radiometric Dating

Part II

Half-lives Passed	Parent Remaining	Daughter Produced	P - D Ratio	P - D Percents
1	1/2	1/2	1:1	50/50
2	1/4	3/4	1:3	25/75
3	1/8	7/8	1:7	12.5/87.5
4	1/16	15/16	1:15	6.25/93.75

1) If a specimen is determined to have 1/4 of its original amount of uranium^{235}, the ratio of uranium^{235} to lead^{207} would be 1:3.

2) If a specimen is determined to have 1/16 of its original amount of uranium^{235}, the ratio of uranium^{235} to lead^{207} would be 1:15.

3) If a specimen is determined to have a 12.5% of its original parent material present, its parent-daughter ratio would be 1:7.

4) If a specimen is determined to have a 3.125% of its original parent material present, its parent-daughter ratio would be 1:31.

Continuing the same pattern of change, the next row on the table above would look like this:

5	1/32	31/32	1:31	3.125/96.875

5) If a specimen is determined to have a 1:3 parent-daughter ratio, 2 half-lives must have passed since its formation.

6) If a specimen is determined to have a 1:31 parent-daughter ratio, 5 half-lives must have passed since its formation.

See the additional row for 5 half-lives above.

7) After the passage of 3 half-lives, the remaining amount of parent material in a specimen would be only 12.5% of the original.

8) After the passage of 4 half-lives, the parent-daughter ratio in a specimen would be 1:15.

9) After the passage of 5 half-lives, the fraction of daughter product in a specimen would be 31/32.

See the additional row for 5 half-lives above.

Radioactive Parent	Stable Daughter	Half-life
Potassium^{40}	Argon^{40}	1.25 billion years
Rubidium^{87}	Strontium^{87}	48.8 billion years
Thorium^{232}	Lead^{208}	14 billion years
Uranium^{235}	Lead^{207}	704 million years
Uranium^{238}	Lead^{206}	4.47 billion years

10) A specimen's uranium^{235}/lead^{207} ratio of 1:3 indicates that 2 half-lives have passed since its formation. Therefore the specimen must be 1.4 billion years old.

The half-life of uranium^{235} (from the table on page 128) is 704 million years.

2 half-lives x 704 million years = 1,408 million years or 1.4 billion years

11) A specimen's uranium^{235}/lead^{207} ratio of 1:31 indicates that 5 half-lives have passed since its formation. Therefore the specimen must be 3.5 billion years old.

The half-life of uranium^{235} is 704 million years.

5 half-lives x 704 million years = 3,520 million years or 3.5 billion years

12) A specimen's potassium^{40}/argon^{40} ratio of 1:7 indicates that 3 half-lives have passed since its formation. Therefore the specimen must be 3.75 billion years old.

The half-life of potassium^{40} is 1.25 billion years.

3 half-lives x 1.25 billion years = 3.75 billion years

13) A specimen's thorium^{232} and lead^{208} contents are analyzed, which indicate that 0.2 half-lives have passed since its formation. Therefore the specimen must be 2.8 billion years old.

The half-life of thorium^{232} is 14 billion years.

0.2 half-lives x 14 billion years = 2.8 billion years

Part III

14) Analysis of a frozen mammoth carcass indicates that the C^{14}/C^{12} ratio of its tissue is 1:31. This means the mammoth died approximately 29,000 years ago.

The half-life of C^{14} (from the Part III text) is 5,730 years.

A 1:31 ratio indicates that 5 half-lives have passed.

5 half-lives x 5,730 years = 28,650 years

Lab 17: Fossils and Stratigraphy

Part I

1) Any remains or evidence of past life are considered to be fossils.

2) One of the most common substances that is preserved by replacement is wood, though it is often said to be "petrified" by non-scientists.

3) The name for fossilized sap or resin is amber.

4) Fossilization by permineralization often creates a fossil that contains some of the original hard parts of the organism reinforced by the precipitated minerals.

5) Molds may be filled by precipitated minerals at times, leading to the formation of a cast.

6) Replacement occurs when mineral matter not only fills the voids in original remains, but also replaces the original hard substances, as well.

7) The voids left by humans' bodies in the hardened ash around Pompeii are called molds.

8) Gastroliths are stones consumed by some animals to aid in digestion.

9) Trace fossils include preserved footprints, tracks, and burrows produced by animals.

10) The fossilized waste of an animal is called a coprolite.

11) Scientists who study past life are called paleontologists.

Fossils to be examined will vary.

Part II

Indicate the type of unconformity illustrated below:

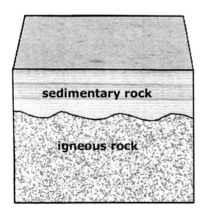 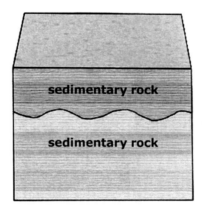 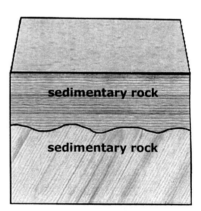

12) nonconformity (igneous rock in contact with sedimentary strata)

13) disconformity (sedimentary strata parallel to sedimentary strata, but separated by non-dep/erosion)

14) angular unconformity (sedimentary strata meeting sedimentary strata at an angle)

oldest D - B - A - E - C - F youngest

D - sedimentary rock (siltstone) is deposited

B - sedimentary rock (sandstone) is deposited

A - sedimentary rock (limestone) is deposited

D, B, and A are deformed/tilted

E - vertical dike intrudes

D, B, A, and E are weathered/eroded

C - sedimentary rock (limestone) is deposited

F - vertical dike intrudes

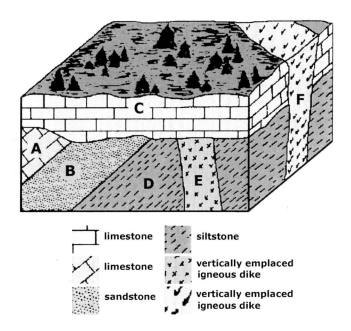

oldest E - D - F - H - J - I - C - B - A - G youngest

E - metamorphic rock (schist) is weathered/
eroded

D - sedimentary rock (conglomerate) is
deposited

F - sedimentary rock (sandstone) is deposited

H - sedimentary rock (siltstone) is deposited

J - sedimentary rock (limestone) is deposited

I - vertical dike intrudes and produces a
laccolith, which deforms J

E, D, F, H, I, and J are deformed/tilted, then
weathered/eroded

C - sedimentary rock (sandstone) is deposited

C is weathered/eroded

B - sedimentary rock (siltstone) is deposited

A - sedimentary rock (limestone) is deposited

G - vertical dike intrudes

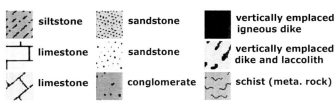

Unconformity #1: nonconformity (metamorphic rock E in contact with sedimentary layers D & F)

Unconformity #2: angular unconformity (sedimentary layers D, F, H, & J meeting sedimentary layer C at
an angle)

Unconformity #3: disconformity (sedimentary layer C parallel to sedimentary layer B, but separated by
non-dep/erosion)

Image Credits